# Antennas for MF and Above

## A guide to practical antennas from 630m to 60m

by

**Mike Parkin, G0JMI**

Published by Radio Society of Great Britain of 3 Abbey Court, Priory Business Park, Bedford MK44 3WH, United Kingdom
**www.rsgb.org.uk**

First Printed 2017

ISBN: 9781 9101 9346 4

Cover design: Kevin Williams, M6CYB
Typography and design: Mark Pressland
Production: Mark Allgar, M1MPA

Printed in Great Britain by

Any amendments or updates to this book can be found at:
www.rsgb.org/booksextra

# Contents

1: Introduction                                               1

2: Overview of Antenna Principles                             3

3: MF Antennas                                                9

4: End-Fed Wire Antennas                                     45

5: Dipole Wire Antennas                                      55

6: Multi-Band Wire Antennas                                  63

7: Directional Antennas                                      81

8: Matching and Antenna Tuning Techniques                    93

   Appendix:  An Overview of WSPR                           103

   References                                               106

# Dedication

To my wife Karen, with thanks for her support, help and patience, during the last year, while I have been working on this book.

# Acknowledgments

I am grateful for the help provided by my friend Tony Green who kindly proof-read my original draft with the aim of ensuring the text was understandable and for identifying typographical mistakes. Tony says he also learnt a lot about antennas too.

My thanks are also passed to Mark Allgar, M1MPA, and to Giles Read, G1MFG, for their encouragement, support and help to me during the writing of this book.

Mike Parkin, G0JMI
September 2017

# Introduction

A radio station for the Medium Frequency (MF) and High Frequency (HF) bands comprises of three fundamental components:

- the MF/HF transceiver and its power supply
- the interconnecting cable between the transceiver and the MF or HF antenna, referred to as the transmission line (or feeder)
- the MF or HF antenna.

The antenna can be considered as the essential link between 'free space' and the transmitter or receiver. Therefore, an MF or HF antenna's role is:

- to ensure that as much of the accessible RF power as possible supplied by the transmitter is radiated as an RF signal
- to ensure that as much of the received RF signal as possible is made accessible as RF power for the receiver to function successfully.

Consequently, the antenna is one of the primary factors that determines the characteristics and effectiveness of the complete system. Therefore, the design of the antenna within its working environment is vital to the overall success of a radio system.

This book provides a practical guide to the construction of MF and lower HF antennas and provides an overview of Antenna Tuning Units (ATU) where applicable. The scale and range of MF and HF antennas is extensive and so this book is confined to the description and construction of the more commonly used antennas on the amateur radio bands from 630m to 60m.

Although most of the antenna designs within this book are intended for the transmission of RF signals, they equally work as reception antennas. Occasional exceptions, eg the receive-only Beverage antenna described in section 7.3, are identified as such.

## Antennas for MF and Above

The amateur allocations for antennas covered within this book are:

| Band | Frequency allocation | Actual wavelengths |
|------|----------------------|--------------------|
| 630m | 472 to 479kHz | 635.59m to 626.31m |
| 160m | 1.81 to 2.0MHz | 165.75m to 150.0m |
| 80m | 3.5 to 3.8MHz | 85.71m to 78.95m |
| 60m | 5.2585 to 5.4065MHz* | 57.05m to 55.49m |

* Note: At the time of writing, unlike the other bands the UK 60m band allocation is not continuous and comprises number segments that collectively are referred to as '60m'.

### 1.1 Scope of this Book

A chapter providing an overview of antenna theory for both MF and HF antennas leads into a series of chapters covering antenna designs for use on the bands between 630m and 60m. The design and construction of MF antennas tend to be of a more specialised nature compared to the design and construction of antennas for the HF bands. Therefore, MF antennas intended for use on the 630m band are described within a dedicated chapter. Antennas for use on the HF bands up to 60m are examined with chapters covering end-fed antennas, dipoles, doublets and directional antennas. A chapter overviewing antenna tuning techniques has been included as an introduction to matching an antenna to the radio equipment so as to obtain the best performance.

### 1.2 Main Abbreviations Used

To follow is a list of the abbreviations used in the chapters to follow:

| | | | |
|------|------------------------------------|------|------------------------------------|
| agl | above ground level | m | length in metres |
| ATU | Antenna Tuning Unit | MF | Medium Frequency (usually 300kHz to 3MHz) |
| dB | decibel | | |
| dBd | dB referred to a dipole | MHz | megahertz (hertz expressed in multiples of $10^6$) |
| dBi | dB referred to an isotropic radiator | | |
| | | P | power in watts (W) |
| ERP | effective radiated power | pF | picofarad (multiples of $10^{-12}$ farads) |
| EIRP | effective isotropic radiated power | | |
| f | frequency in Hz | $Po_{Tx}$ | transmitter's output power supplied at the feed point in watts (W) |
| FSD | Full scale deflection of a meter | | |
| HF | High Frequency (usually from 3MHz to 30MHz) | | |
| | | RF | radio frequency |
| Hz | hertz or RF cycles per second | $R_{loss}$ | Loss resistance of the antenna |
| I | current in amperes | RMS | root mean square |
| Icm | common mode current | $R_{rad}$ | radiation resistance of the antenna |
| $I_{ant}$ | current flowing in the antenna | | |
| kHz | kilohertz (hertz expressed in multiples of $10^3$) | SWR | standing wave ratio |
| | | UK | United Kingdom |
| $k\Omega$ | multiples of a thousand ohms | W | Power expressed in watts |
| L | inductance in henries | $\lambda$ | wavelength in metres |
| $L_{ant}$ | inductance associated with a loop antenna | $\Omega$ | resistance in ohms |

# Overview of
# Antenna Principles

The information to follow has been included as a guide to understanding the practicalities involved with MF and HF antennas in terms of their design, construction and performance.

The *Radio Communication Handbook* [1] and *LF Today* [2] provide detailed guidance covering the operation and construction of MF and HF antennas. The information to follow provides an overview with an emphasis on operating on the bands from 630m to 60m.

## 2.1 Wavelength, Antenna Length and Feed Point

The wavelength (λ) of an RF signal travelling in free space is given by:

$$\lambda\,(\mathrm{m}) = \frac{300}{f}$$

where f is the frequency in MHz and λ is in metres (m).

Many antennas are based on using a wire span whose length is an electrical half-wavelength (λ/2) long. The RF signal to be transmitted, or to be received, can use a connection at either the antenna's centre or at one of its ends. The position where the antenna is supplied with, or receives, the RF signal is referred to as the feed point. When the antenna is fed at its centre, this antenna is usually referred to a dipole. However, when the antenna is fed at one of its ends, this is usually referred to as being an end-fed antenna.

A λ/2 long antenna is often referred to as a resonant antenna. The voltage and current distributions along the antenna are not uniform and are approximately sinusoidal, as shown in Figure 2.1 (overleaf). For an electrically λ/2 long antenna, the voltage at the ends of the antenna is high while the current is close to zero. However, at the antenna's centre the opposite situation occurs with the current high and voltage close to zero. When the feed point is located at one end of an electrically λ/2 long antenna, then this coincides with a voltage maximum and is referred to as being voltage fed. Either end of the wire span could be used as the feed point for an end-fed antenna. The impedance at a voltage feed point will be high and of the order of 5kΩ. Locating the feed point at the centre of an electrically λ/2 long antenna coincides with a current maximum and this is referred to as being current fed and the impedance is low.

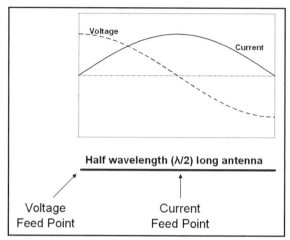

Figure 2.1: Concept of the voltage and current distributions along a λ/2 antenna and their relationship to the feed point.

Generally, the physical length of λ/2 long antenna is given by:

$$\text{Length}(m) = \frac{150(n - 0.05)}{f} \tag{1}$$

Where n is the number of complete half-waves along the antenna's wire span and f is the frequency in megahertz (MHz).

This equation allows for several factors that can affect the physical length of the antenna for true resonance. These factors act to cause a slight retardation of the wave's velocity along the wire and so reduce its length slightly. They include:

- the effect of RF radiation
- the dielectric coating on the wire
- the end-insulators that can introduce additional capacitance.

The capacitance contributed by the insulators used to terminate the antenna's ends is termed 'end-effect'.

Therefore, for a practical horizontally installed λ/2 antenna (where n = 1), its physical length can be calculated using:

$$\text{Length}(m) = \frac{150 \times (0.95)}{f} \tag{2}$$

However, for a practical λ/4 vertical antenna, where end-insulators are not an issue, its physical length can be calculated using:

$$\text{Length}(m) = \frac{75 \times (0.98)}{f} \tag{3}$$

## 2.2 Radiation Resistance and RF Power Radiated

An antenna is made from a conductive material, such as aluminium or copper, and this will have a resistance (Rc). When RF power is delivered from the transmitter into the antenna, this will cause an RF current (I) to flow within the antenna. Some of the RF power delivered will be lost because of the heating effect from Rc. Using ordinary circuit relationships, this power loss is given by $I^2$.Rc watts.

However, the majority of the RF power will usually be radiated as an electromagnetic wave by the antenna. Given that electrical power can only be consumed by a resistance, it is convenient to consider the radiated RF power as dissipated in a fictitious resistance and this known as the radiation resistance (Rrad) of the antenna. If an RF current (I) is flowing into the radiation resistance (Rrad), then an RF power of $I^2$. Rrad watts is being radiated by the antenna.

It is therefore necessary to specify the point of reference for the current when determining the value of the Rrad and it is usual to assume the point of maximum current. An example of an antenna fed at a current maxima is the centre-fed half wave ($\lambda/2$) dipole in free space. This antenna has a radiation resistance of about $(73 + j43)\Omega$ and the antenna is slightly inductive. Making the length of the dipole slightly shorter introduces a capacitive effect that for practical purposes cancels the inductance, leaving a radiation resistance of $73\Omega$ resistive (as included within equations 1 to 3 for a practical antenna's length summarised previously). However, the height of a horizontally installed resonant $\lambda/2$ dipole above the ground will also have an influence on Rrad. As the height of the resonant dipole increases compared to the wavelength ($\lambda$) of operation, so Rrad tends towards a value of around 70 to $80\Omega$.

## 2.2 Antenna Efficiency and Performance

For an antenna that is installed horizontally with respect to the ground, particularly a dipole, if the antenna is made of a good conductive material, such as copper or aluminium, then any RF power loss due to the conductor's resistance (Rc) is very small (Rc is often less than $1\Omega$). Consequently, the conductor's RF power loss is relatively small compared to the radiated RF power and the antenna provides an efficient coupling between the transmitter and free space.

However, the situation for a vertical antenna differs compared to a horizontal antenna because its operation depends upon the antenna being worked against the ground. A vertical antenna's efficiency can be analysed in terms of three main components:

- the antenna's capacitance ($C_A$)
- the antenna's radiation resistance (Rrad)
- the antenna's resistive loss ($R_{loss}$).

Although Rrad is relevant to the performance of both horizontally and vertically orientated antennas, the values of $C_A$ and $R_{loss}$ have more of significant influence for a vertical antenna. The concept of a

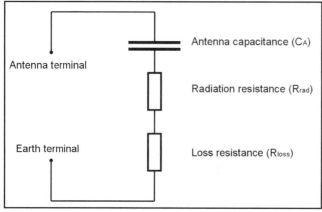

Figure 2.2: Equivalent circuit of a vertical antenna.

vertical antenna comprising these components is shown as Figure 2.2. The effect of $C_A$ and $R_{loss}$ on a vertical antenna is summarised in the next sections.

### 2.2.1 Antenna Capacitance

For a vertical antenna, its performance is influenced by the antenna capacitance ($C_A$) that comprises a vertical capacitive component ($C_V$) and a horizontal component ($C_H$). The effect of $C_A$ on the performance of a vertical antenna is examined within Chapter 3.

For a horizontally installed antenna, it is the antenna's end-capacitance that can have a major effect on the performance of the antenna. The type of insulator used at the wire span's ends influences the antenna's end-capacitance and some types of insulator can introduce more capacitance than others (eg the 'egg' shaped insulator introduces more than a 'dog bone' type).

### 2.2.3 Loss Resistance

For a vertical antenna, the loss resistance ($R_{loss}$) can be significant depending upon the design of the antenna and its working environment. Compared to a horizontally installed antenna, it is $R_{loss}$ that can have a major influence on the performance of a vertical antenna. Many MF antenna designs are vertical antenna derivatives, therefore $R_{loss}$ is considered referred to a vertical antenna in the following description.

The loss resistance ($R_{loss}$) represents the proportion of the power fed to a vertical antenna that is lost, being dissipated as heat in the antenna wire, tuner, ground and any lossy objects near the antenna. In amateur antennas, $R_{loss}$ is invariably much larger than Rrad.

$R_{loss}$ can be found by measuring the RF resistance at the vertical antenna's feed point when the antenna is tuned to resonance. This measurement gives Rrad + $R_{loss}$, however for a vertical MF antenna $R_{loss}$ is much larger than Rrad and this measurement can be taken as equal to $R_{loss}$.

$R_{loss}$ could also be found by measuring the transmitter's output power ($Po_{Tx}$) and the MF vertical antenna's current (Iant) when the antenna is at resonance:

$$\mathrm{Rloss}\left(w\right)=\frac{Po_{Tx}}{Iant^{2}} \qquad [4]$$

For vertical antennas, where the antenna is worked against ground, the contribution to $R_{loss}$ by the ground's resistance can be significant and this can often vary from around under 10Ω to over 200Ω depending upon the ground's physical characteristics.

## 2.3 Vertical antenna efficiency

$R_{loss}$ becomes important to consider when determining the efficiency of a vertical antenna in terms of the RF signal radiated. The radiated RF power (Prad) efficiency is given by:

$$\text{Prad efficiency}\,(\%)=Po_{Tx}\times\left(\frac{R_{rad}}{(R_{rad}+R_{loss})}\right)\times100\% \qquad [5]$$

where $Po_{Tx}$ is the transmitter's output power supplied at the feed point.

The efficiency of a vertical MF antenna is examined within Chapter 3.

## 2.4 The Isotropic Radiator and its Relationship to other Antennas

If an antenna could be made minutely small and feederless, then theoretically the antenna would equally radiate RF energy in all three dimensions and the overall radiation pattern would be a sphere. Although the construction of such an antenna is not possible, it is used as a reference antenna when assessing antennas and is known as an isotropic radiator or isotropic source [3]. When measuring an antenna's performance in terms of its gain, or loss, in dB this is often referred to an isotropic radiator and this measurement is stated in dBi. Figure 2.3(a) shows the concept of an isotropic radiator and its spherical radiation pattern.

The simplest practical form of antenna is the dipole. Although this antenna may be of any length, the word 'dipole' usually implies an electrically half wavelength ($\lambda/2$) long resonant antenna, fed via a balanced feeder at the centre. The dipole antenna does not radiate equally in all directions because the current along its length is not constant and it produces a three dimensional 'toroidal-shaped' radiation pattern. Figure 2.3(b) shows the concept of dipole radiating an RF signal

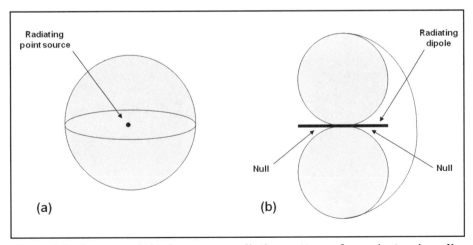

**Figure 2.3: Concept of the free space radiation patterns for an isotropic radiator and a dipole antenna. For an isotropic radiator, shown in (a), the radiation pattern is a sphere. For a dipole, shown in (b), the radiation pattern is a toroid symmetrically oriented along the axis of the wire span.**

and its toroidal shaped radiation pattern. The dipole is also used as a reference antenna and has a power gain of 2.15dB over an isotropic radiator, or 2.15dBi. Measurements of the gain, or loss, in dB of an antenna using the half wavelength ($\lambda/2$) dipole antenna as a reference are stated in dBd.

To calculate the gain of an antenna in dBd, 2.15dB is taken off the antenna's gain quoted in dBi. Mathematically, 2.15dB equates to a gain of close to 1.64 times. For example, if an antenna has a gain quoted as 7.15dBi, then its gain referred to a dipole is 5dBd.

## 2.5 Antenna Transmit and Receive Reciprocity

The performance of an antenna is normally the same for both the transmit and the receive modes of operation and this is termed reciprocity. Therefore, when considering the design of a transmitting antenna, its performance when used to receive signals will be the same. When examining the performance of an antenna, reciprocity allows the antenna to be examined either when transmitting or receiving, whichever is the more convenient

# MF Antennas

The MF amateur band covers 472 to 479kHz in the UK, corresponding to a wavelength ranging from around 636m to 626m. Therefore, this is referred to as the 630m band.

Theoretically, a $\lambda/2$ antenna for use on the 630m band is going to be around 300m in length. When installed horizontally above the ground, this represents a significantly long antenna, making it impractical to install within the space available at most domestic locations. Also, to enable the antenna to become an effective RF radiator, the $\lambda/2$ antenna needs to be installed at a height of at least $\lambda/4$ agl, or around 160m (or higher). Such a height further adds to the impracticalities of installing a $\lambda/2$ antenna for the 630m band at most domestic locations.

A $\lambda/4$ vertical antenna, when installed in an upright position to the ground, for the 630m band is around 156m high. The antenna is worked against ground with the feed point located between the bottom of the antenna and the ground itself. At around 156m agl, this also represents a significantly high antenna, again making it impractical to install at most domestic locations.

Therefore, a 630m band antenna has to be a compromise and this effects its efficiency as an RF radiator. The underlying principles of antennas are the same at 472kHz as at other frequencies. However, with an operating wavelength of around 630m, practical amateur radio MF antennas can only be 'electrically small' with a physical length that is a fraction of a wavelength. This results in the antenna being operated very much below its self-resonant frequency, requiring a large amount of inductive and/or capacitive loading to enable a resistive load to be presented to the transmitter. An electrically small MF antenna can be expected to be very inefficient, typically under 2% efficient for a back-garden installation.

Electrically small antennas fall into two types: vertical or loop. In the UK and Europe the majority of amateurs have used vertical antennas on

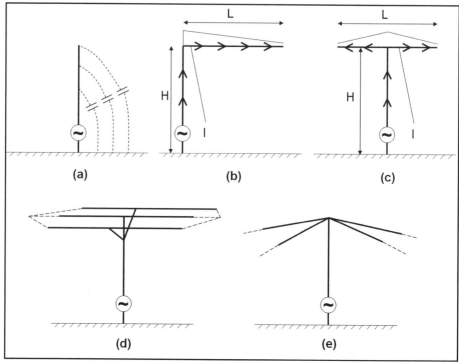

**Figure 3.1: Vertical antenna configurations with the concept of RF current flow and capacitance to ground indicated.**

the 630m band, however loop antennas have been popular with operators in North America.

## 3.1 Vertical Antennas

The vertical or Marconi antenna is a widely used MF transmitting antenna consisting of a vertical monopole element, whose length is a small fraction of a wavelength long. This antenna is worked against a ground plane as shown in Figure 3.1(a) and the voltage along the element is nearly equal at all points along its length. However, the current is a maximum at the feed point and tapers to zero at the antenna's end. This is because the current flows to the ground plane through the distributed capacitance of the antenna element as shown.

### 3.1.1 Determining the Effective Height of a Vertical Antenna

The non-uniform current distribution along a real vertical antenna has an effect where the RF radiated field takes on the form of that for a theoretical antenna with a uniform current distribution of a shorter length. The length of this theoretical antenna is referred to as the effective height ($H_{eff}$) of the real vertical antenna. The nearer $H_{eff}$ is to the vertical antenna's actual length, so the better the performance of the antenna. The antenna's $H_{eff}$ can be increased by adding an arrangement to load the top of the vertical element and this is referred to as top-loading. Examples of top-loading include the T and inverted-L configurations, as shown in Figures 3.1(b) and 3.1(c).

In either the T or inverted-L configurations, the distributed capacitance of the vertical section ($C_V$) and the horizontal section ($C_H$) is given approximately by:

$$C_V(pF) = \frac{24H}{Log_{10}\left(\frac{1.15H}{d}\right)} \tag{6}$$

$$C_H(pF) = \frac{24L}{Log_{10}\left(\frac{4H}{d}\right)} \tag{7}$$

where:

H is the height of the vertical section (m)
L the length of the horizontal section (m)
d is diameter of the wire (m) including its plastic insulation if present
$C_V$ and $C_H$ are in picofarads (pF)

As an approximation:

$C_V$ is about 6pF/m of length
$C_H$ is about 5pF/m of length.

A technique to maximise the top loading effect, when the amount of space is limited, is to use multiple top-loading wires to form a 'flat-top' T antenna, as shown in Figure 3.1(d). As a result of proximity effects, multiple parallel wires have less capacitance compared to a single wire of the same total length. As a guide, two 1mm wires spaced 100mm apart will have about 39% greater capacitance than a single wire over the same span, while spacing them 1m apart will increase the capacitance by 68% compared to the single wire.

Once $C_V$ and $C_H$ are known, then the effective height ($H_{eff}$) of the top-loaded vertical antenna can be determined from its physical height (H) in metres using:

$$H_{eff}(m) = H \times \left(\frac{\frac{2C_H}{C_V}+1}{\frac{2C_H}{C_V}+2}\right) \tag{8}$$

With no top-loading, then $C_H = 0$ and so $H_{eff} = H/2$ (ie half the height of the real vertical antenna). Conversely, with a very large top loading capacitance, then $C_H$ is much larger $C_V$ and $H_{eff}$ is nearly equal to H (ie close to the actual height of the real vertical antenna). Therefore, adding a large amount of top-loading can nearly double the $H_{eff}$ of the vertical section. The actual shape of the top loading arrangement used is not very important; the main objective is to maximise its capacitance.

Another form of vertical antenna often used at MF is the umbrella, as shown in Figure 3.1(e). This top-loading technique consists of sloping wires, with the advantage that only a single tall support is required. The drawback to this technique is the current flowing in the sloping wires will have a 'downwards' component that partly cancels the 'upwards' current of the vertical section. If the ends of the loading wires are brought close to ground level, this tends to reduce the antenna's performance because the $H_{eff}$ becomes too small. Therefore, the far ends of the loading wires should not be lower than half the height of the central vertical section to maintain the beneficial effects available from using this technique. The formulas for the T and inverted-L antennas can still be used to calculate the approximate $H_{eff}$ of an umbrella antenna. However, this requires the modification that H is now the average height of the sloping wires, rather than the highest vertical point of the antenna, with L now taken as the horizontal length of the sloping wires.

Often an existing HF dipole or long wire antenna can be used as a basis for an MF antenna. The antenna's horizontal wire-span allows a large proportion of the antenna current to flow to ground through the distributed capacitance, so increasing the current flowing in the upper part of the vertical section. When a dipole or doublet antenna is used, the usual practice is to connect the feeder cable's conductors together at the bottom, thus making a single wire to form the MF antenna's vertical section.

### 3.1.3. Determining the Radiation Resistance ($R_{rad}$)

The impedance of a vertical antenna can be represented by a series combination of $R_{rad}$, $R_{loss}$ and $C_A$ (as previously shown in Figure 2.2). $R_{rad}$ is the radiation resistance and represents the conversion the transmitter's power ($PO_{Tx}$) into radiated RF signal. $R_{rad}$ is related to $H_{eff}$ and to the wavelength ($\lambda$) of the radiated signal in metres by equation (9):

$$R_{rad} = \frac{160 \times \pi^2 \times \left(H_{eff}\right)^2}{\lambda^2}$$
[9]

MF antennas generally present a very low $R_{rad}$ and often this can be a fraction of an ohm. The power radiated from the antenna as electromagnetic waves is $I_{ant}^2 \times R_{rad}$ (watts), so a large $I_{ant}$ (antenna current) is required for appreciable power to be radiated by the antenna.

### 3.1.4 Loss Resistance $R_{loss}$ and Efficiency

The other resistive component of the antenna's impedance is the loss resistance ($R_{loss}$) representing the power losses in the antenna and its surroundings. Therefore, $R_{loss}$ includes the:

- resistance of the antenna wires
- resistance of ground system
- power dissipated due to dielectric losses in the ground under the antenna
- Power dissipated by objects near the antenna (eg trees and buildings).

Power dissipated in $R_{loss}$ is converted into heat and is, therefore, wasted. The same antenna current flowing in $R_{rad}$ also has to flow through $R_{loss}$. Therefore, a measure of the antenna's efficiency is given by the ratio:

$$\text{Antenna efficiency} = \left(\frac{R_{rad}}{R_{rad} + R_{loss}}\right) \times 100\% \qquad [10]$$

For an MF antenna, $R_{rad}$ is typically very small compared to $R_{loss}$ and an approximation of the antenna's efficiency is given by:

$$\text{Approximate antenna efficiency} = \left(\frac{R_{rad}}{R_{loss}}\right) \times 100\% \qquad [10a]$$

$R_{loss}$ depends very much on the environment around the antenna and there is no really reliable way of determining $R_{loss}$ by theoretical calculation. Measured $R_{loss}$ values for typical amateur antennas in the MF band range from around 10 to 200Ω, with larger antennas having a lower $R_{loss}$ of typically around 30Ω at 472kHz. Methods used to reduce $R_{loss}$ are examined later within this chapter in section 3.6, Ground Systems.

### 3.1.5 Radiation Pattern

Although the horizontal parts of a vertical antenna wire are often much longer than the vertical section, little horizontally polarised RF radiation is generated. This is because, when the height of the horizontal section is a small fraction of the wavelength, the effect of the horizontally-flowing current is almost completely cancelled out by the equal but opposite 'image' current flowing in the ground plane, as shown in Figure 3.2(a). Consequently, these antennas are still classed as verticals with the vertical section being the primary radiator, consequently the radiation produced is almost entirely vertically polarised.

The radiation pattern of any electrically short vertical antenna is virtually the same. It is omnidirectional in the azimuth (horizontal) plane, meaning the antenna radiates uniformly in all directions and has a field strength that is pro-

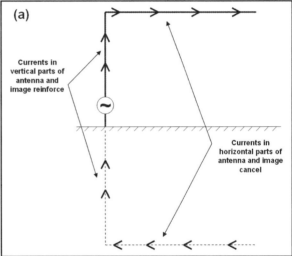

Figure 3.2(a) Concept of cancellation of the horizontally-polarised RF radiation, while vertically-polarised RF reinforces.

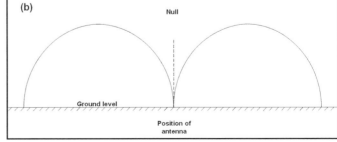

Figure 3.2(b) Theoretical concept of a typical MF short vertical antenna radiation pattern.

portional to the cosine of elevation. This gives rise to maximum radiation towards the horizon and a null vertically upwards. The theoretical radiation pattern for an electrically short vertical antenna is shown in Figure 3.2(b).

### 3.1.6 Gain of Electrically Short Vertical Antennas

It may seem implausible for an electrically short vertical monopole antenna, when worked against the ground, to exhibit gain over a dipole antenna. However, when examined in the vertical plane, the antenna's RF radiation becomes concentrated towards the horizon. This effect gives rise to the vertical antenna developing gain as measured by a receiving station situated at a distance perpendicular to the transmitting vertical. This effect was investigated several decades ago, with several studies conducted into the RF radiation distribution patterns of electrically short vertical antennas when worked against the ground. Two such studies were performed by Dr Stuart Ballantine, who reported that as the frequency of the operation was increased for the same length of vertical monopole, when worked against the ground, so the antenna's gain was found to improve.

The IET (formerly the IEE) *Handbook of Antenna Design Volume 2* [4] summarises the gains (in dBd) that can be expected for an electrically short vertical antenna, when worked against the ground, whose length is a fraction of the wavelength ($\lambda$) of operation as shown in Table 3.1. The gain of an electrically short vertical antenna is close to 2.62dB with respect to a dipole, or x 1.83 as a power ratio, irrespective of their shape and size.

### 3.2 Effective Radiated Power (ERP)

At the time of writing, the schedule contained in the UK Amateur Licence conditions specifies a maximum power level for the 472 to 479kHz band (630m) as 5W (7dBW) Effective Isotropic Radiated Power (EIRP).

The calculation of EIRP is referred to the gain between the antenna in use and an isotropic radiator. Consequently, when assembling a 630m band station, it is important to have an understanding of the concept of radiated power and methods of determining EIRP.

The gain of the antenna can be considered to be the product of the antenna's efficiency and its directional gain (directivity) compared to a theoretical reference isotropic radiator antenna operating on 630m.

### 3.2.1 Estimating EIRP

The EIRP can, in principle, be determined from a knowledge of the transmitter's power, antenna efficiency and directivity. Antenna efficiency can

| Vertical Antenna Length | Gain | Approximate Power Ratio |
|---|---|---|
| Much less than $\lambda/4$ | 2.62dBd | 1.83 |
| $\lambda/4$ | 3.01dBd | 2.00 |
| $\lambda/2$ | 4.68dBd | 2.94 |
| 0.53$\lambda$ | 5.03dBd | 3.18 |
| 0.64$\lambda$ | 6.03dBd | 4.00 |

Table 3.1: Gains that can be expected from electrically short vertical antennas, using data from [4].

be estimated by calculating the radiation resistance $R_{rad}$ as described previously, then measuring the loss resistance ($R_{loss}$) using an RF bridge or similar. Multiplying the transmitter output power ($Po_{Tx}$) by the efficiency gives the total radiated power ($P_{rad}$):

$$P_{rad}\left(W\right) = Po_{Tx} \times \left(\frac{R_{rad}}{R_{rad}+R_{loss}}\right)$$

Where $Po_{Tx}$ is the transmitter's output power in watts (W) supplied at the feed point.

Another way to find $P_{rad}$ is to measure the RF current ($I_{ant}$) flowing at the antenna feed point. Then, $P_{rad}$ in watts (W) is given by:

$$P_{rad}\left(W\right)=(I_{ant})^2 \times R_{rad} \qquad [11]$$

The Effective Radiated Power (ERP) is then given by $P_{rad}$ multiplied by the gain with respect to a dipole (2.62dB, or 1.83 times, as described previously):

$$P_{rad}\left(ERP\ in\ watts\right)=1.83 \times (I_{ant})^2 \times R_{rad}$$

To calculate the Effective Isotropic Radiated Power (EIRP), $P_{rad}$ (ERP) is then multiplied by 1.64 (this equates to 2.15dB, or the gain of a dipole over an isotropic radiator):

$$P_{rad}\left(EIRP\ in\ watts\right)=1.64 \times (P_{rad}\ ERP)$$

or:

$$P_{rad}\left(EIRP\ in\ watts\right)=1.64 \times (1.83) \times \left(I_{ant}\right)^2 \times R_{rad}$$

This equation simplifies to:

$$P_{rad}\left(EIRP\ in\ watts\right) = 3 \times \left(I_{ant}\right)^2 \times R_{rad} \qquad [12]$$

## 3.3 Measuring the Antenna Current ($I_{ant}$)

Measuring the antenna current ($I_{ant}$) allows a reasonable estimation of the antenna's radiated power to be determined using equation (11), shown just earlier:

$$P_{rad}\left(W\right)=(I_{ant})^2 \times R_{rad} \qquad [11]$$

A good practice is to use a thermojunction RF ammeter as a means to

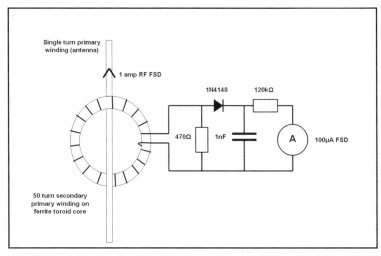

**Figure 3.3(a): RF ammeter circuit based on a ferrite toroid core.**

measure $I_{ant}$. However, for most radio amateurs, a thermo-junction RF ammeter can be difficult to obtain. Therefore, another way to measure $I_{ant}$ is to construct an RF ammeter, as described in [1] [5] [6].

An example of a RF ammeter having a full-scale deflection of 1 amp is shown in Figure 3.3(a). This comprises a ferrite toroid core that forms an RF current transformer comprising a:

- single-turn primary winding consisting of the current-carrying antenna wire threaded through the toroid
- secondary winding of 50 turns wound onto the toroid core.

This arrangement forms a step-down current transformer and the secondary current is 1/50 of the primary current. If the primary current is 1 amp RMS, the secondary current is 20mA RMS and this develops a voltage of 9.4V RMS across the 470Ω load resistor. This voltage is measured by a diode voltmeter and the peak voltage across the 1nF smoothing capacitor is 1.414 x $V_{RMS}$, or 13.3V. To account for the forward voltage drop across the diode (about 0.5V), this gives approximately 12.8V DC. The meter used had a full scale deflection (FSD) of 100µA; the 120kΩ series resistor sets the meter to full scale deflection indicating 1 amp RF current RMS flowing into the antenna. The RF ammeter's current range can be increased by proportionally reducing the

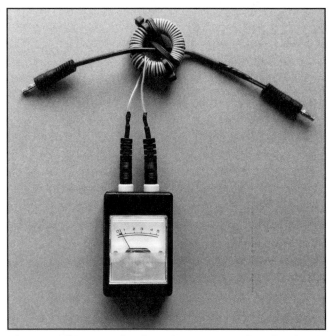

**Figure 3.3(b): Example of an RF ammeter using the circuit from Figure 3.3(a). The reading on the meter is multiplied by 4 to give the reading in volts.**

value of the load resistor, however it is desirable to maintain the voltage across the load at around 10V to maintain the linearity of the diode voltmeter. It should be noted that with higher maximum currents, the power dissipation in the load resistor can become significant, so the resistor needs to be appropriately rated.

A high permeability ferrite core is required for the circuit to ensure that the impedance of the secondary winding is much larger than the impedance presented by the load-resistor/meter circuit. A toroid core with a permeability of 5000 or above should be used. The 50 turn secondary should typically present an inductance of several millihenries (mH).

Figure 3.3(b) illustrates an example of an RF ammeter built using the guidance above and the circuit shown in Figure 3.3(a). The meter reading was multiplied by four to give a reading in volts.

A split ferrite core could be used to allow the ammeter to be put into the circuit without disconnecting the antenna wire. If the RF ammeter is to be used at a high voltage point, such as at the feed point of the antenna wire, then it is advisable to screen the transformer and meter circuit using a metal case to enclose the circuit. This avoids the possibility of stray currents flowing in the meter circuit due to capacitive coupling, which can cause erroneous readings.

## 3.4 A Worked Example

As the basis for an antenna used to operate on 474kHz, consider a horizontally installed 80m band dipole centred on 3.65MHz with a wire diameter of 2mm. Using equation (2), this antenna's wire span was cut to be 39m long. This span was centrally fed using a 10m long balanced twin-line cable, brought vertically downwards. The balanced twin-line cable's ends were shorted to form the vertical section of the MF antenna.

### 3.4.1 Horizontal and Vertical Capacitance

Using equations (6) and (7), the distributed capacitance of the dipole's vertical section ($C_V$) and the horizontal section ($C_H$) is given approximately by:

$$C_V\ (pF) = \frac{(24 \times 10)}{Log_{10}\left(\dfrac{1.15 \times 10}{0.002}\right)} = \mathbf{64pF}$$

$$C_H\ (pF) = \frac{(24 \times 39)}{Log_{10}\left(\dfrac{4 \times 10}{0.002}\right)} = \mathbf{218pF}$$

$C_V + C_H$, or 64pF + 218pF = 282pF

### 3.4.2 Calculating the Effective Height (H$_{eff}$) of the Antenna

Using the equation (8), the effective height (H$_{eff}$) of the 80m band dipole can be calculated as follows.

with

$$C_V = 64pF$$
$$C_H = 218pF$$

then:

$$\text{Heff}(m) = 10 \times \left( \frac{\dfrac{2\times218pF}{64pF}+1}{\dfrac{2\times218pF}{64pF}+2} \right) = \textbf{8.87m}$$

This is slightly shorter than the actual length (H) of 10m.

### 3.4.3 Calculating the Radiation Resistance (R$_{rad}$) of the Antenna

The radiation resistance (R$_{rad}$) represents the conversion of transmitter power (PO$_{Tx}$) into radiated RF signal. R$_{rad}$ is related to H$_{eff}$ and to the wavelength ($\lambda$) of the radiated signal in metres. Using equation (9):

$$\text{Rrad} = \frac{160\times\pi^2\times\left(\text{Heff}\right)^2}{\lambda^2} \tag{9}$$

Taking 474kHz (633m) as the frequency of operation:

$$\text{Rrad} = 0.00394 \times \left(\text{Heff}\right)^2$$

Using the example above with a H$_{eff}$ of 8.87m:

$$\text{Rrad} = 0.00394 \times \left(8.87\right)^2 = \textbf{0.31}\boldsymbol{\Omega}$$

To summarise, an antenna with 8.87m effective height (H$_{eff}$) has a radiation resistance (R$_{rad}$) of only 0.31 ohms at 474kHz. The power radiated from the antenna as an electromagnetic wave is I$_{ant}^2$ x R$_{rad}$ (watts), so a large antenna current is required for appreciable power to be radiated by the antenna.

### 3.4.4 EIRP and Calculation of the Maximum Antenna Current (I$_{ant}$)

If the permitted radiated power for a UK amateur radio station operating on the 630m band is 5 watts EIRP then, using equation (12):

$$\text{Prad (EIRP in watts)} = 3 \times \left(\text{Iant}\right)^2 \times \text{Rrad}$$

Rearranging the equation gives:

$$I_{ant} = \sqrt{\frac{\left(P_{rad}\left(EIRP \text{ in watts}\right)\right)}{\left(3 \times R_{rad}\right)}}$$

A reasonable indication of the maximum value of $I_{ant}$ can then be found from:

$$I_{ant} = \sqrt{\frac{\left(5 \text{ watts EIRP }\right)}{\left(3 \times 0.31\Omega\right)}} = \textbf{2.319 amps RMS}$$

### 3.4.5 Summary

For this particular 80m dipole antenna fed using a shorted 10m long twin-line cable, to radiate a power of 5 watts EIRP, the maximum antenna current ($I_{ant}$) should not exceed 2.319 amps RMS.

Note: A power of 5 watts equates to an EIRP of 7dBW (power in dB referred to a watt), or 4.85dBd (power in dB referred to a watt to a dipole).

### 3.5 Practical Antenna Considerations

An existing HF antenna whose horizontal wire span is installed between two high points can be used as the basis for a 630m band antenna. As previously described, the HF antenna's feeder cable can be used as the vertical section of the 630m band antenna provided the end of the twin-conductor cable is short-circuited, thus forming a single feeder wire that is connected to the matching arrangement. An existing centrally fed dipole, doublet, Off Centre Fed Dipole (OCFD) or end-fed wire can be brought into service as a 630m band antenna as appropriate. The effective height ($H_{eff}$) of the 630m band antenna depends upon the length of the HF antenna's vertical section (ie the shorted feeder cable or feeder wire) and the length of its horizontal wire-span. Consequently, the $H_{eff}$, $R_{rad}$, ERP and EIRP calculations equally apply for each of these HF antenna configurations.

Compared to the magnitude of the antenna current ($I_{ant}$) flowing in a vertical antenna of the same height as the HF antenna's vertical section, $I_{ant}$ flowing in the vertical section can be increased as a result of the wire-span forming a capacitor with the ground below it. This concept is shown was shown previously in Figure 3.2(a), where an equal but opposite current flows in the ground compared to the horizontal wire span. The longer the wire-span, so the higher the capacitance formed to ground and the larger current flowing through the ground enhancing $I_{ant}$ flowing in the vertical section. This increase in $I_{ant}$, in turn, increases the antenna's ERP. Using the wire-span in this way to enhance the performance of the antenna is referred to as top-loading.

The antenna's primary radiator is the vertical section and the horizontal wire-span tends not to radiate the RF signal because the current flowing in it is equal but opposite to the current flowing in the ground. Consequently, these currents tend to cancel each other resulting in negligible radiation from the horizontal wire-span (as previously described). When an antenna is top-loaded in this manner, the antenna is classed

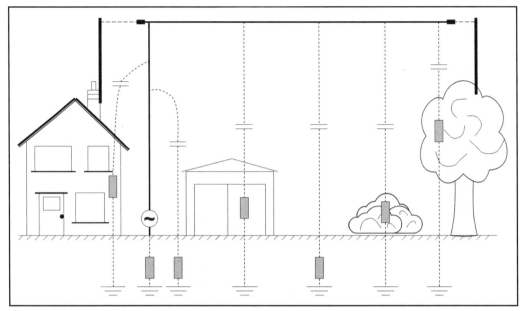

**Figure 3.4: Loss in the environment around an antenna.**

as vertical antennas because of the vertical section being the primary radiator of the RF signal.

To maximise the performance of the antenna, the vertical section should be:

- brought perpendicularly straight down from the wire-span's feed point with the station situated directly below if possible
- ideally not be run close to any objects or structures in the vicinity of the vertical section.

Any close objects or structures can become electrically coupled to the radiating vertical section, reducing the antenna's performance. However, remotely locating the vertical section from close objects or structures is not always a practical possibility in domestic locations (eg the house, neighbouring houses, trees, shrubs and other out-buildings for example). As a guide, the concept of objects or structures that could affect the performance of a 630m band antenna are shown in Figure 3.4. Essentially, these objects and structures provide undesirable routes for some of $I_{ant}$ to be leaked to ground, reducing the performance of the antenna. Therefore, when at all possible, the vertical section and the horizontal wire span should be run as far away from any objects as feasible.

### 3.5.1 Using a Full-Size G5RV Antenna as a 630m Band Antenna

The G5RV multi-band antenna is described in greater detail in Chapter 6, Multi-Band Wire Antennas. However, it can be used as a basis for a 630m band antenna.

A G5RV antenna is often thought of as a wire-span of 31.1m long that is centrally fed using about 10.38m of air-spaced ladder-line ca-

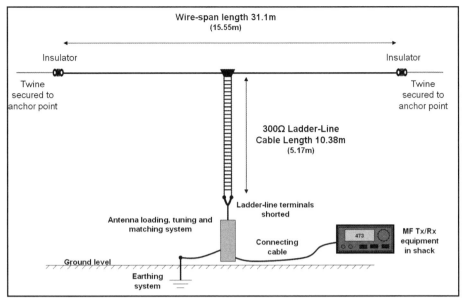

Figure 3.5(a): Using a G5RV antenna as the basis for a 630m band Marconi T type antenna (dimensions shown in brackets are for the half-size G5RV antenna).

ble. Many G5RV antennas use commercially available 300Ω ladder-line cable as the feeder and this has a different velocity factor compared to an air-spaced feeder cable. Consequently, when 300Ω ladder-line cable is used, its length is around 9.5m. This configuration is often referred to as the full-size G5RV and covers the bands from 80m to 10m. The concept of the full-size G5RV antenna used for the 630m band is shown in Figure 3.5(a).

For the purposes of the analysis to follow, the length of the short-circuited feeder cable has been taken as 10m and it has been assumed that this feeder cable acts solely as the radiating vertical section. The length of the wire-span used is 31m and it has a diameter of 2mm.

### Capacitance:
Using equations 6 and 7, the distributed capacitance of the dipole's vertical section ($C_V$) and the horizontal section ($C_H$) is given approximately by:

$$C_V(pF) = \frac{(24 \times 10)}{Log_{10}\left(\frac{(1.15 \times 10)}{0.002}\right)} = \mathbf{64pF}$$

$$C_H(pF) = \frac{(24 \times 31)}{Log_{10}\left(\frac{(4 \times 10)}{0.002}\right)} = \mathbf{173pF}$$

**21**

### Effective Height:

Using the equation 8, the effective height ($H_{eff}$) can be calculated as follows:

with

$$C_V = 64pF$$
$$C_H = 173pF$$

then:

$$H_{eff}(m) = 10 \times \left( \frac{\frac{(2\times173pF)}{64pF}+1}{\left(\frac{2\times173pF}{64pF}\right)+2} \right) = \mathbf{8.65m}$$

### Radiation Resistance:

The radiation resistance ($R_{rad}$) can be calculated using equation (9):

$$R_{rad} = \frac{160\times\pi^2\times(H_{eff})^2}{\lambda^2}$$

Taking 474kHz (633m) as the frequency of operation:

$$R_{rad} = 0.00394 \times (H_{eff})^2 = 0.00394 \times (8.65)^2 = \mathbf{0.295\Omega}$$

### Maximum Antenna Current ($I_{ant}$)

Using the permitted radiated power of 5 watts EIRP and using equation 12:

$$P_{rad}(\text{EIRP in watts}) = 3 \times (I_{ant})^2 \times R_{rad}$$

Rearranging the equation gives:

$$I_{ant} = \sqrt{\frac{(P_{rad}(\text{EIRP in watts}))}{3\times R_{rad}}}$$

A reasonable indication of the maximum value of $I_{ant}$ can then be found from:

$$I_{ant} = \sqrt{\frac{(5\text{ watts EIRP})}{3\times0.295\Omega}} = \mathbf{2.38\text{ amps RMS}}$$

## Predicted Radiation Pattern

The G5RV antenna was modelled using the MMANA-GAL antenna modelling application [7] to predict its radiation patterns. The antenna was modelled with the horizontal 31m long wire span at 11m agl, with the 10m long short-circuited feeder cable running straight down from the centre of the wire span. The G5RV antenna's predicted radiation pattern in the horizontal plane was omnidirectional, meaning the antenna radiates uniformly in all directions, as could be expected for a vertical antenna. The predicted radiation pattern in the vertical plane indicates that much of the radiation is directed towards the horizon with a null verti-

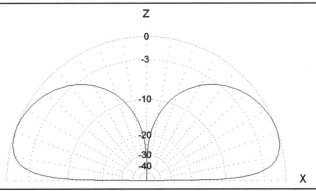

Figure 3.5(b): MMANA-GAL prediction of the antenna's radiation pattern in the vertical plane.

cally upwards above the antenna, as shown in Figure 3.5(b). This should favour contacts being made with near stations through ground wave propagation. However, more distant stations may be heard/worked because the low angle radiation towards the horizon may give rise to longer-skip skywave propagation depending upon the condi-

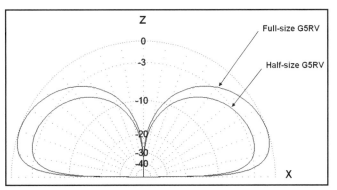

Figure 3.5(c): MMANA-GAL comparison of the vertical plane predictions for the half-size G5RV and full-size G5RV antenna radiation patterns.

tions for MF ionospheric propagation. The radiation directed skywards between 10° to 60° should enable contacts to be made with more local stations through shorter-skip skywave propagation, again, depending on the MF conditions.

### 3.5.2 Using a Half-size G5RV Antenna as a 630m Band Antenna

Another version of the antenna is the half-size G5RV, where the wire-span's length is 15.55m and is centrally fed using about 5.17m of air-spaced ladder-line cable and covers the bands from 40m to 10m. If commercially available 300Ω ladder-line cable is used as the feeder, then this has a different velocity factor compared to an air-spaced feeder cable. Consequently, when 300Ω ladder-line cable is used, its length is around 4.7m. The concept of the half-size G5RV antenna used for the 630m band is also shown in Figure 3.5(a), where the antenna's dimensions are shown bracketed.

For the purposes of the analysis to follow, the length of the short-circuited feeder cable has been taken as 5m and it has been assumed that this feeder cable acts solely as the radiating vertical section. The length of the wire-span used is 15.5m.

### Capacitance:

Using equations (6) and (7), the distributed capacitance of the dipole's vertical section ($C_V$) and the horizontal section ($C_H$) is given approximately by:

$$C_V\,(pF) = \frac{(24 \times 5)}{Log_{10}\left(\dfrac{1.15 \times 5}{0.002}\right)} = \textbf{35pF}$$

$$C_H\,(pF) = \frac{(24 \times 15.5)}{Log_{10}\left(\dfrac{4 \times 5}{0.002}\right)} = \textbf{93pF}$$

### Effective Height:

Using the equation 8, the effective height ($H_{eff}$) can be calculated as follows:

with

$$C_V = 35pF$$
$$C_H = 93pF$$

then:

$$H_{eff}\,(m) = \left(\frac{\dfrac{(2 \times 93pF)}{35pF} + 1}{\dfrac{(2 \times 93pF)}{35pF} + 2}\right) = \textbf{4.32m}$$

### Radiation Resistance:

The radiation resistance ($R_{rad}$) can be calculated using equation (9):

$$R_{rad} = \frac{160 \times \pi^2 \times (H_{eff})^2}{\lambda^2}$$

Taking 474kHz (633m) as the frequency of operation:

$$R_{rad} = 0.00394 \times (H_{eff})^2 = 0.00394 \times (4.32)^2 = \textbf{0.074}\,\mathbf{\Omega}$$

### Maximum Antenna Current ($I_{ant}$):

Using the permitted radiated power of 5 watts EIRP and using equation 12:

$$P_{rad}\,(EIRP\ in\ watts) = 3 \times (I_{ant})^2 \times R_{rad}$$

Rearranging the equation gives:

$$I_{ant} = \sqrt{\frac{(P_{rad}(EIRP\ in\ watts))}{(3 \times R_{rad})}}$$

A reasonable indication of the maximum value of $I_{ant}$ can then be found from:

$$I_{ant} = \sqrt{\frac{(5 \text{ watts EIRP})}{(3 \times 0.074\Omega)}} = \mathbf{4.75\,amps}$$

### *Predicted Radiation Pattern:*

The half-size G5RV antenna was modelled using the MMANA-GAL antenna modelling application [7] to predict its radiation patterns. The antenna was modelled with the horizontal 15.5m long wire span at 6m agl, with the 5m long feeder cable running straight down from the centre of the wire span.

The half-size G5RV antenna's predicted radiation pattern in the horizontal plane was omnidirectional in a similar way as that for the full-size G5RV antenna. The antenna's radiation pattern in the vertical plane is shown compared to the larger size version in Figure 3.5(c). The half-size G5RV antenna's radiation pattern is very similar to that for the full-sized G5RV antenna. However, the half-sized G5RV antenna's performance can be seen to be around 3dB down compared to the larger version.

### 3.5.3 Using an End-Fed Antenna as a 630m Band Antenna

For the purposes of analysis, an end-fed wire antenna in an inverted-L configuration has been used. The concept of this antenna is shown in Figure 3.6(a), where the horizontal wire span is 20m long that is fed with a single wire of 8m long with a diameter of 2mm. It has been assumed that the single-wire feeder acts solely as the radiating vertical section.

**Note:** The analysis to follow also applies to an OCFD antenna (covering the bands from 40m through to 10m) and a dipole cut for the 40m band (centred on 7.1MHz) of the same dimensions.

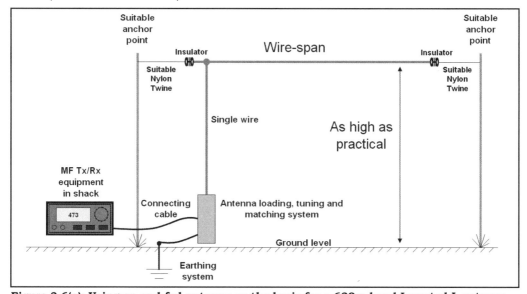

**Figure 3.6(a): Using an end-fed antenna as the basis for a 630m band Inverted-L antenna.**

### Capacitance:

Using equations (6) and (7), the distributed capacitance of the dipole's vertical section ($C_V$) and the horizontal section ($C_H$) is given approximately by:

$$C_V(pF) = \frac{(24 \times 8)}{Log_{10}\left(\frac{(1.15 \times 8)}{0.002}\right)} = \textbf{52pF}$$

$$C_H(pF) = \frac{(24 \times 20)}{Log_{10}\left(\frac{(4 \times 8)}{0.002}\right)} = \textbf{114pF}$$

### Effective Height:

Using the equation 8, the effective height ($H_{eff}$) can be calculated as follows:

with

$C_V = 52pF$
$C_H = 114pF$

then:

$$H_{eff}(m) = 8 \times \left(\frac{\frac{(2 \times 114pF)}{52pF} + 1}{\frac{(2 \times 114pF)}{52pF} + 2}\right) = \textbf{6.75m}$$

Radiation Resistance: The radiation resistance ($R_{rad}$) can be calculated using equation (9):

$$R_{rad} = \frac{160 \times \pi^2 \times (H_{eff})^2}{\lambda^2}$$

Taking 474kHz (633m) as the frequency of operation:

$$R_{rad} = 0.00394 \times (H_{eff})^2 = 0.00394 \times (6.75)^2 = \textbf{0.18}\Omega$$

### Maximum Antenna Current ($I_{ant}$)

Using the permitted radiated power of 5 watts EIRP and using equation (12):

$$P_{rad}(\text{EIRP in watts}) = 3 \times (I_{ant})^2 \times R_{rad}$$

Rearranging the equation gives:

$$I_{ant} = \sqrt{\frac{(P_{rad}\,(\text{EIRP in watts}))}{(3 \times R_{rad})}}$$

A reasonable indication of the maximum value of $I_{ant}$ can then be found from:

$$I_{ant} = \sqrt{\frac{(5 \text{ watts EIRP})}{(3 \times 0.18\Omega)}} = \textbf{3.04 amps}$$

### Predicted Radiation Pattern

The inverted-L antenna was modelled using the MMANA-GAL antenna modelling application [7] to predict its radiation patterns. The antenna was modelled with the horizontal 20m long wire span at 9m agl, with the 8m long feeder cable running straight down from the end of the wire span. The antenna's predicted radiation pattern in the horizontal plane was omnidirectional as could be expected for a vertical antenna. The antenna's performance in the horizontal plane was about the same as that predicted for the full-size G5RV antenna. The antenna's radiation pattern in the vertical plane is shown in Figure 3.6(b) for both the Marconi T and inverted-L configurations for comparison. Both the configurations of the antenna show predictions in the vertical plane that do not significantly differ, although the T configuration has a more pronounced null directly above the vertical section. The predicted radiation patterns for both configurations of the antenna are very similar to that predicted for the full-size G5RV and should give a similar performance.

## 3.6 Ground Systems

To maximise the performance of a Marconi type antenna it is necessary to use a ground system. This is to help overcome some of the losses that are associated with returning the antenna current back to the antenna's feed point through the ground. Consequently, the conductivity of the soil under the MF antenna influences its efficiency and performance. This effect of the soil's conductivity on the MF antenna's performance can extend for some distance around the antenna. Clay-based soil can be useful because it tends to hold moisture, increasing conductivity and lowering the losses. However, sand and rock tend to be poor because moisture tends to drain through them, increasing the losses. Sea water is ideal and stations situated close to the sea can be at a greater advantage.

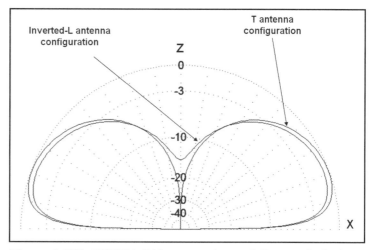

**Figure 3.6(b): MMANA-GAL comparison of the vertical plane predicted radiation patterns for the inverted-L end-fed antenna and a centrally fed T antenna of the same dimensions.**

# Antennas for MF and Above

**WARNING: Protective Multiple Earthing (PME)**

Many houses in the UK are wired on what is known as the PME system. In this system the earth conductor of the consumer's installation is bonded to the neutral close to where the supply enters the premises and there is no separate earth conductor going back to the sub-station. Under certain rare supply fault conditions a shock or fire risk could occur where external conductors such as antennas or earths are connected. For this reason the supply regulations require additional bonding and similar precautions in PME systems.

Many houses in UK were wired on the old TN-S system, where a separate earth goes back to the sub-station. In such systems there were no problems with connecting an external radio antenna or earth. It has recently become evident that changes to maintenance and installation practice mean that the inherent safety of the old TNS systems cannot always be guaranteed. The situation is being reviewed. **Until further information is available all installations should be treated as if they were PME.** Note that PME is also designated as TN-CS by the IET Wiring Regulations BS 7671, which follows the appropriate IET documents.

Read the RSGB leaflet EMC 07 Earthing and the Radio Amateur [8] before connecting any earth or antenna system to equipment inside the house. The leaflet is available free from the RSGB EMC Committee website or on request from RSGB HQ.

**If in doubt consult a qualified electrician.**

You should also check to see whether Building Control must be informed before starting any work.

Amateur radio MF stations have been operated from all types of terrain, so do not be discouraged: poorer soils just need more work and ingenuity to overcome the losses associated with the ground.

To maximise the performance for any Marconi type antenna, a ground system is required. The ground system most widely used consists of a number of ground rods connected to a common point close to the antenna feed point. This type of ground system has been found to work well where soil conductivity is quite high. As an approximate guide, a 1m long ground rod has a resistance of around of 20Ω. When several ground rods are used that are spaced a few metres apart, this resistance figure is roughly divided by the number of rods. However, a point is quickly reached where the ground system resistance becomes only a few ohms and any further improvements to the ground system results in a very small reduction in overall loss resistance. If a large number of ground rods are used, it has been found that relatively little RF current flows in the rods that are placed further away from the feed point. This effect is understood to be caused by the distributed inductance associated with the longer length of the wire needed to connect the remoter rods to the rest of the ground system. The distributed inductance is thought to make the longer wire's impedance become significant enough to limit the current flowing. However, where the ground conductivity is very low this effect may not be a problem and a ground system distributed over a wider area could be expected to give a useful improvement. Unfortunately, not much information or data is available on this subject.

Earth rods intended for domestic mains earthing are ideal as ground rods. These are designed to be rigid enough to allow them to be hammered into the ground without deforming. It is also possible to use copper water pipe, unfortunately this material tends to buckle when being driven into the ground. However, copper pipes could be used as a ground rods where the ground is soft, or they could be inserted into pre-made holes. The rods should be as long as possible and be in contact with permanently damp soil to maximise their effect. Ground systems of buried radial wires, as used for HF vertical antennas, have also proved effective for use with a 630m band antenna.

Commercial MF, LF and VLF radio stations use hundreds of kilometres of wire spread out over a radius of several hundred metres as the ground system for their antennas. Often, wire mesh matting is buried to improve the ground system that can

**PLANNING PERMISSION**

In the UK and many other parts of the world permission is required before antennas or their supports above a certain (small) height may be erected. Procedures vary by country, even between England, Scotland, Wales and Northern Ireland. Tolerance of antennas and their supports may vary from town to town according to local arrangements. For instance, a 25m mast topped by multiband Yagis would probably be unwelcome in a picturesque village but might gain permission in a different rural area with good tree cover – though not somewhere sensitive like the Green Belt, an Area of Outstanding Natural Beauty or a National Park.

It is a good idea to get planning advice before committing time or money on a permanent antenna project: more than one person has had to sell off a new mast cheaply because they were refused planning permission.

There is some general guidance available on the RSGB website, and RSGB Members can get free, detailed advice on UK planning matters from the RSGB Planning Advisory Committee.

contain many kilometres of buried wire. However, for amateur radio MF antennas, it is usually possible to produce a ground system that has a negligible contribution to overall antenna loss because other losses in the antenna system are much higher.

## 3.7 Custom-built MF Antennas

When planning to set up an MF antenna, there are two significant considerations to be taken into account:

- the height of the antenna above the ground
- the extent of the antenna's coverage across the ground.

The effective height ($H_{eff}$) of the antenna above the ground is a function of the actual vertical section of the antenna and the configuration of the horizontal section. $H_{eff}$ has a square law influence on the antenna's radiated power, so it is important to make the vertical section as high as practical and avoid too much sag on the horizontal sections. This may involve several support poles around the periphery of the location (eg garden), plus one pole in the centre to support the vertical section. However, in practice, every system involves a compromise to enable the antenna to be installed within the space available. The horizontal top-loaded section of a Marconi antenna (often termed the capacity hat) can be of any shape and often the most popular and practical are the inverted-L and T configurations. To maximise the antenna's performance, at a given location, the top section should cover as much of the ground area available as possible.

In a similar way as previously described for an HF antenna configured for use as a 630m band antenna, if possible the MF antenna's
location should be clear of RF absorbers including trees and shrubs.
The top wires must not touch any part of a tree because this will lead
to losses and unpredictable performance. Good practice is to keep all
wires a few metres away from trees where possible. Similarly, avoid
running wires above tall shrubs, or prune the shrubs down first. The
antenna should be sited clear of buildings where possible, eg the house,
garage or outbuildings (as previously shown in Figure 3.4). However,
the antenna arrangement chosen depends how much ground area is
actually available to allow a number of high supports to be erected and,
importantly, how tolerant the neighbours are. Another consideration to
be aware of is if planning permission is required for antenna system?

### 3.7.1 Multi-wire T or Inverted-L Antenna Configurations

A single very long horizontal wire span can be extremely effective,
especially if it is at a good height (eg 15m agl or more). However, the
antenna's performance can be improved by using a multi-wire top
section forming a T or an inverted-L configuration. An example of
an inverted-L antenna using a parallel multiple-wire top is shown in
Figure 3.7. Where possible, joining the ends of the parallel wires can
improve the antenna's performance because this can increase antenna's
capacitance, particularly if the wires are spaced far apart. However,
the aim is to install as much wire as possible between the supports
(eg tall trees) as shown in the example of Figure 3.8 for a multi-wire T

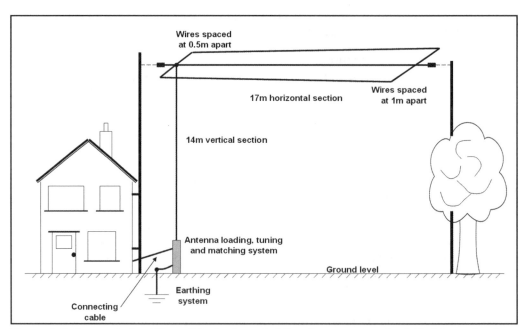

**Figure 3.7: Concept of an MF multi-wire inverted-L antenna system installed in a suburban
environment using a house-mounted mast and another mast strapped to a tall tree (based
on the antenna set up used by G3XDV).**

antenna. In this T antenna configuration the multiple wires should be as far apart as possible to maximise the performance of the antenna.

### 3.7.2 Umbrella Configuration Antenna

Another capacity hat configuration used by commercial MF stations is the umbrella, as shown in Figure 3.9. This type of antenna is often used for non-directional beacons (NDB), among other applications. The top-loading consists of sloping wires, with the advantage that only a single central tall support is required. With only two top-loading wires, the umbrella becomes an inverted-V, or with one wire it becomes a sloping long wire.

The drawback to this antenna is that the current flowing in the sloping wires will have a 'downwards' component that partly cancels the 'upwards' current of the vertical section. Bringing the ends of the loading wires close to the ground tends to reduce the effective height ($H_{eff}$) of the antenna. Many combinations of length and angle of slope are possible, however provided the lower ends of the loading wires are at least half the height of the central vertical element, the overall effect of the umbrella top loading will be beneficial.

The formulas for the T and inverted-L antennas can still be used to calculate the approximate effective height of the umbrella, with the modification that the vertical section's height (H) is now the average height of the sloping wires, rather than the highest vertical point of the antenna, and the horizontal section's length (L) is the horizontal length of the sloping wires.

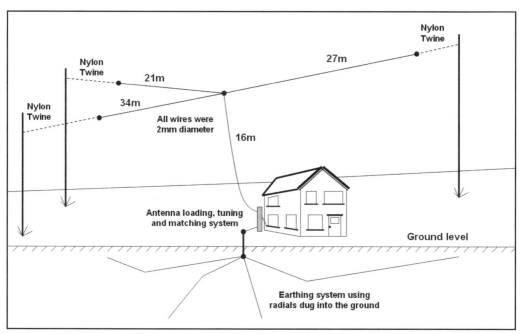

**Figure 3.8: Concept of an MF multi-wire T antenna system comprising a top section of different lengths of wire (based on the antenna setup used by OK1FIG).**

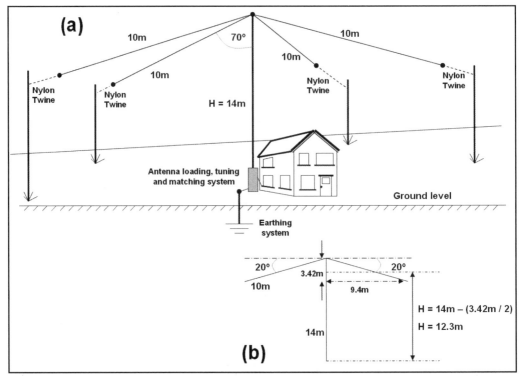

**Figure 3.9: (a) Concept of an umbrella antenna configuration and (b) the average height of the antenna used to determine H_eff. All antenna wires were 2mm diameter.**

Figure 3.9(a) illustrates the concept of an umbrella antenna using four span-wires connected to a central vertical section wire, where:

- each span-wire's length is 10m, running straight without sagging
- each span-wire makes an angle of 70° to the central vertical section wire
- the central vertical section wire's length is 14m
- the wire used had a diameter of 2mm.

Figure 3.9(b) illustrates the average height (12.3m) and span length (4 x 9.4m, or 37.6m) of the antenna used to calculate the capacitance, $H_{eff}$, $R_{rad}$ and $I_{ant}$ as follows:

**Capacitance:**
Using equations (6) and (7), the distributed capacitance of the dipole's vertical section ($C_V$) and the horizontal section ($C_H$) is given approximately by:

$$C_V\,(pF) = \frac{(24 \times 12.3)}{Log_{10}\left(\frac{(1.15 \times 12.3)}{0.002}\right)} = \textbf{76.7pF}$$

$$C_H\,(pF) = \frac{(24 \times 15.5)}{Log_{10}\left(\frac{(4 \times 5)}{0.002}\right)} = \textbf{205.5pF}$$

### Effective Height:
Using the equation (8), the effective height ($H_{eff}$) can be calculated as follows.

with

$C_V = 76.7pF$
$C_H = 205.5pF$

then

$$Heff(m) = 12.3 \times \left( \frac{\left( \frac{2 \times 205.5pF}{76.7pF} \right) + 1}{\left( \frac{2 \times 205.5pF}{76.7pF} \right) + 2} \right) = \mathbf{10.63m}$$

### Radiation Resistance:
The radiation resistance ($R_{rad}$) can be calculated using equation (9):

Taking 474kHz (633m) as the frequency of operation:

$$Rrad = 0.00394 \times (Heff)^2 = 0.00394 \times (10.63)^2 = \mathbf{0.45\Omega}$$

### Maximum Antenna Current ($I_{ant}$):
Using the permitted radiated power of 5 watts EIRP and using equation (12):

$$Prad(EIRP \text{ in watts}) = 3 \times (Iant)^2 \times Rrad$$

A reasonable indication of the maximum value of $I_{ant}$ can then be found from:

$$Iant = \sqrt{\frac{(5 \text{ watts EIRP})}{(3 \times 0.45\Omega)}} = \mathbf{1.925\,amps\,RMS}$$

### Predicted Radiation Pattern:
The umbrella antenna was modelled using the MMANA-GAL antenna modelling application [7] with antenna's apex at 15m agl. The antenna's predicted horizontal and vertical plane radiation patterns were almost identical to those for the full-size G5RV antenna and a similar performance can be expected.

## 3.8 Safety Considerations with MF Antennas
Practical MF antennas tend to be short compared to the wavelength that they are designed to be operated on. As a consequence of this, the RF voltage at all points along an MF antenna tends to be nearly equal. The RF voltage is approximately equal to the antenna current ($I_{ant}$) multiplied by the capacitive reactance of the antenna ($C_A$) and can be significantly

high. For example, taking the umbrella antenna configuration previously described, where the value of IA was 1.925A and $C_A$ was 282.2pF then:

$$\text{The antenna's reactance in } \Omega = \frac{1}{2 \times \pi \times f \times C_A}$$

Taking f = 474kHz and $C_A$ as 280pF, then:

$$= \frac{1}{2 \times \pi \times 474pF \times 280pF} = 1200\Omega$$

Antenna RF voltage ≈ 1.925 x 1200 = 2,310 volts

Therefore, whilst transmitting, anyone who comes into contact with this MF antenna at high RF power could receive an RF burn, even possibly without direct contact.

For any MF transmitting antenna, care must be taken to ensure that nobody and nothing (including pets) can come into contact with any part of the antenna while connected, unless the coax screen and any support metalwork has been bonded to the main earthing terminal. If not it is advisable to make sure that access to the antenna is restricted to ensure that no-one can get too close to it.

Also, it is possible for large metal objects (ladders, garden furniture, metal-framed greenhouse, metal guttering etc) near the antenna to have a significantly high RF voltage induced into them when the antenna is operating, which could cause someone an RF burn if they touch the object. It is best to avoid metal objects as far as possible and run lower power if you only have a small garden. However, if you can touch the antenna from standing on the ground, then the coax screen on its cable needs to be bonded back to the main earthing terminal in the house.

### 3.9 Matching Techniques

In principle, to match an MF antenna to the transmitter/receiver, the same matching networks can be used as those utilized for HF antenna matching. These include, for example, the T or Pi-network tuner circuits that could be used to match vertical antennas on 630m. However, if these circuits are used on 630m the component values become impracticably large and tend to require very high ratings owing to the high antenna voltages encountered, particularly so for the tuning capacitors. The two most popular MF antenna matching circuits are shown in Figure 3.10(a) and Figure 3.10(b).

In Figure 3.10(A), to resonate the antenna system, the series loading coil has an inductive reactance that cancels out the capacitance of the antenna ($C_A$). Consequently, the remaining resistive component of the impedance is practically equal to the loss resistance ($R_{loss}$). This is then matched to transmitter's 50Ω output impedance, or other value of transmitter output impedance, using a ferrite-cored transformer. The capacitance of an amateur antenna installed in a domestic location is typically a few hundred picofarads (pF) necessitating a loading

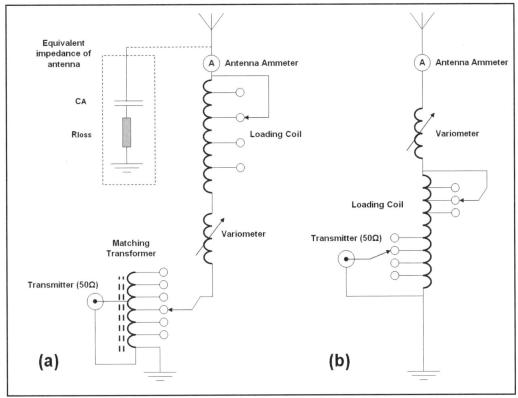

**Figure 3.10: Two examples of tuning arrangements. (a) MF antenna tuner. (b) Alternative antenna tuning circuit.**

inductance of a few hundred microhenries (µH) to resonate the system on the 630m band. Since the antenna reactance is much larger than the resistive component, the loading inductor must be capable of fine adjustment to obtain resonance accurately. Coarse adjustment is usually achieved by a series of taps on the loading coil. However, for fine tuning, the inductance is made variable over a narrow range using a variometer. For most 630m band vertical antennas, $R_{loss}$ often lies between around 10 to 200Ω, requiring a transformer with a turns ratios of between about 1:2 to 2:1 to match the 50Ω transmitter output to the antenna system. One design of 630m matching transformer used an ETD29 transformer core made from 3C90 ferrite material, wound with around 30 turns of 1.5mm enamelled copper wire, tapped every two turns. The 50Ω transmitter output was connected to the mid-turn tapping point, with the 'cold' end of the loading coil connected to the tap that gave optimum matching. This matching arrangement tends to be straightforward to use because the adjustment of antenna resonance and resistance are almost independent of each other. ETD29 cores can sometimes be found at radio rallies and they can also be sourced from online suppliers. Figure 3.11 (overleaf) shows an example of the arrangement shown in Figure 3.10(a) used by Jim Moritz, M0BMU, on 630m to tune his antenna system.

**Figure 3.11: 472 – 479kHz antenna tuning system used by M0BMU.**

Another matching network that is often used is shown in Figure 3.10(b). This network uses a tapped loading coil to match the transmitter's output to the 630m antenna system. The low potential end of the loading coil is wound with closely-spaced taps. This is to enable the loading coil to act as a matching auto-transformer. Although the physical arrangement is less complicated compared to that shown in Figure 3.10(a), the electrical behaviour of this circuit is more complicated. The loading coil's primary and secondary auto-transformer windings are not tightly coupled, consequently the transformer impedance ratio does not closely correspond to the turns ratio. Therefore, the adjustment of the antenna to resonance and the selection of the appropriate impedance-matching tap tend to be interdependent. However, with trial and error, a suitable tapping point can be found and, once found, this should not need to be changed.

The range of antenna loss resistance ($R_{loss}$) that can be matched using the tapped loading coil depends on the coil's geometry. In general, if the coil has a reasonably small diameter and coarse winding pitch (ie it is wound with thick wire), the maximum value of $R_{loss}$ that can be matched is quite low. If the coil has larger diameter and has a fine winding pitch, then a much higher $R_{loss}$ can be matched. However, this latter coil arrangement is then less suitable for low resistance antennas because the required tap tends to be just a few turns from the grounded end of the coil, resulting in the adjustment of the matching being coarse. Another disadvantage of the tapped coil matching arrangement is that the variometer is connected to the 'hot' (high voltage) end of the of the coil, so any adjustments have to done using (very) low power and attention must be given to the insulation on the adjuster. A Microsoft Excel spreadsheet is available for calculating similar curves for any coil diameter and winding pitch [9].

**Figure 3.12(a): 472 – 479kHz loading coil and combined 'telescoping' variometer antenna tuning system used by G0JMI.**

**Figure 3.12(b): The outer and inner coils comprising the 472 – 479kHz antenna tuning system used by G0JMI.**

Figure 3.12(a) illustrates an example of the technique shown in 3.10(b) in use, however the system shown also comprised an integral variometer used to resonate the system. A summary of the details and construction of the variometer technique is described later within this chapter.

### 3.9.1 Loading Coil Considerations

The loading coil's inductance (L) in association with the capacitance of the MF antenna ($C_A$) is used to bring the system to resonance. This is to enable a near-resistive load to be presented to the transmitter to maximise the antenna's radiated RF signal. Therefore, the resonant frequency ($f_{res}$) of the antenna closely approximates to:

$$fres(Hz) = \frac{1}{2 \times \pi \times \sqrt{L \times CA}} \qquad [13]$$

Rearranging equation (13) allows an indication of the inductance (L) to be calculated that is required to resonate the antenna system:

$$L(Henries) = \frac{1}{4 \times \pi^2 \times fres^2 \times CA} \qquad [13a]$$

Using the antenna example from Section 3.5.3 for a 20m long wire span fed by an 8m long vertical section, then the inductance is given by:

$$L = \frac{1}{4 \times \pi^2 \times (474kHz)^2 \times 166pF} = 680\mu H \qquad [14]$$

where $f_{res}$ has been taken as 474kHz and the value of $C_A$ of 166pF (ie $C_H$ + $C_V$ or 114pF + 52pF, from Section 3.5.3).

The approximate number of turns required to wind an inductor is given by equation (14) [10]:

$$Number\ of\ turns \approx \frac{\sqrt{(457.2) \times (L) \times (D) + (1016 \times Len \times L)}}{D}$$

Where L is the coil's inductance (in μH), D is the coil's diameter of the coil (mm) and Len the length of the coil (in mm). If the loading coil is 240mm long, of diameter 50mm and its required inductance is 680μH, then using equation (14) gives the number of turns as

$$\frac{((457.2 \times 680 \times 50) + (1016 \times 240 \times 680))^{\frac{1}{2}}}{50} \approx 270\ turns$$

This indicates that a loading coil of around 270 turns is required to resonate the antenna system on 474kHz. A good practice is to add a few extra turns when the coil is wound. They can be removed if found necessary when tuning. However, for the loading coil, a number of taps should be included when the coil is wound, as illustrated in Figure 3.10(b). Consequently, if the loading coil is wound with a few additional turns, then the appropriate taps can be found when tuning the antenna system. Figure 3.12(b) shows an example of the loading coil calculated above (right side coil) used to resonate a 20m long OCFD antenna on the 630m band. The former used for the loading coil was 50mm diameter PVC external grade tube and the winding used insulated stranded copper wire of 1mm diameter.

It is worthwhile re-running the calculations above for the full-size G5RV antenna (31m long with a feeder length of 10m, described in Section 3.5.1) at 474kHz. Taking the value of $C_A$ as 237pF calculated previously for a G5RV antenna (ie $C_A = C_V + C_H$, or 64pF + 173pF), then from equation (13a):

$$L = \frac{1}{4 \times \pi^2 \times (474\text{kHz})^2 \times 237\text{pF}} = 476\mu\text{H}$$

For an inductance of 476µH, and using the same dimensions for this coil, the number of turns is now approximately

$$\frac{\left((457.2 \times 476 \times 50) + (1016 \times 240 \times 476)\right)^{\frac{1}{2}}}{50} \approx 225 \text{ turns}$$

A loading coil of only around 225 turns is required to resonate the G5RV antenna system on 474kHz because its capacitance is significantly higher compared to using the 40m dipole.

## 3.10 Variometers

A variometer provides a mechanism to fine tune a loading coil's inductance to enable the antenna system to be brought to resonance. A commonly used form of variometer is shown in Figure 3.13(a) consisting of two coils, where one coil is able to be rotated inside the other. When the coils are aligned, the magnetic fields become additive. This results in the mutual inductance between the coils adding to the self inductance of each coil, giving the maximum overall inductance. Conversely, rotating the inner coil by 180° results in the magnetic fields opposing each other. This results in the mutual inductance between the coils subtracting from the self inductance of each coil, giving minimum overall inductance. An adjustment range of about 2:1 in inductance is possible using this technique. An example of this technique used by Jim Moritz, M0BMU is shown in Figure 3.11, while another example constructed by Jean, F6HCC, is shown in Figure 3.14 [11]. Reference [12] includes an on-line calculator for designing the Figure 3.13(a) form of variometer.

Another form of variometer is shown in Figure 3.13(b) where two coils are 'telescoped' together to vary the mutual inductance. An example of this technique is shown in Figure 3.12(a) where the loading coil and variometer are combined. This antenna tuning system used two coils that were wound onto PVC tubes of 70mm and 50mm outside

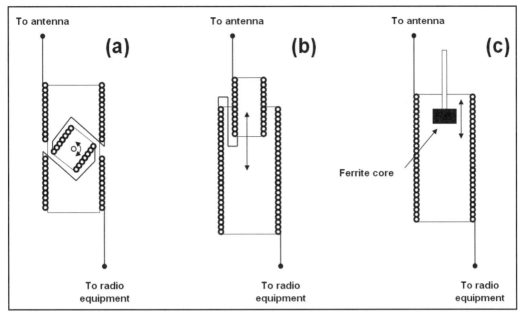

**Figure 3.13: Three variometer techniques used to tune an MF antenna (see text).**

diameter. The larger 70mm diameter outer coil comprised 193 turns of 5A insulated stranded copper wire, while the inner 50mm diameter coil consisted of 200 turns of 0.7mm insulated stranded copper wire. To resonate the antenna, it was found necessary to add an additional coil of 60 turns connected in series with the 200 turns coil as shown (also wound using 0.7mm insulated stranded copper wire). The outer larger diameter coil was tapped 57 turns from its lower (earthed) end where a good match to the transmitter's output impedance was found. This arrangement enabled a Marconi T antenna comprising a 20m long wire span and vertical 8m section to be resonated for operation on the 630m band. The optimum position of the inner coil was found by monitoring the maximum antenna current, using an RF ammeter (see Figure 3.3), as the inner coil was moved up/down inside the outer coil. Once the optimum position of the inner coil had been found, the coil was held in place using an insulated wedge. Figure 3.12(b) shows two coils used to make the 'telescopic' variometer.

An arrangement that involves only one coil is shown in Figure 3.13(c). Here a ferrite core is used for permeability tuning of an air-cored coil. This arrangement

**Figure 3.14: Example of a variometer tuning system consisting of two coils, where one coil is able to be rotated inside the other, as used by F6HCC.**

could comprise a coil of a few hundred microhenries inductance that is wound on a horizontal tube former. The ferrite core is glued to a plastic handle and is free to slide inside the tube. For this arrangement, it is important to use a short and thick piece of ferrite rather than a long rod. This is because flux density associated with using a long ferrite rod can become very high, leading to saturation and severe heating of the core. A large switch-mode power supply transformer core works well for this arrangement.

### 3.11 Loop Antennas used for Transmitting

MF Loop antennas have tended to be more popular with amateurs in North America than in the UK or Europe, where most amateurs have used vertical antennas on the 630m band. While the vertical antenna is a high voltage and relatively low current device, conversely the loop antenna is a relatively low voltage and high current device. The loop antenna has the advantage that it works well in locations where there are many vertical objects, such as trees, that tend to adversely affect a vertical antenna. The transmitting loop antenna has a 'figure-of-eight' radiation pattern in the azimuth plane, with deep nulls at right angles to the plane of the loop (that can be of the order of 20dB).

The impedance of the loop can be modelled as the loop inductance in series with a radiation resistance $R_{rad}$ and a loss resistance $R_{loss}$. The value of $R_{rad}$ depends on the area of the loop (A) in square metres ($m^2$), where:

$$\text{Rrad}\ (\Omega) = 2 \times 320 \times \pi^2 \frac{N^2 \times A^2}{\lambda^4} \qquad [15]$$

where N is the number of turn (usually one) and $\lambda$ is the wavelength in metres.

The factor of 2 is included in the formula to take into account the effect of the ground plane underneath the loop. This, in principle, can double $R_{rad}$ and is caused from the 'image' antenna reflected in the ground plane.

For example, if the operating frequency is 474kHz (ie 630m) with a vertical rectangular loop antenna of 40m by 15m (ie 600m$^2$), then:

$$\text{Rrad}\ (\Omega) = 2 \times 320 \times \pi^2 \left( \frac{1^2 \times 600^2}{633^4} \right) = 0.014\Omega$$

The dominant source of losses for a loop antenna is the RF resistance of the loop conductor. To achieve reasonable efficiency, very thick wire, or multiple parallel wires should be used. Some amateurs have resorted to using the braid of UR67 coaxial cable, or even copper water pipe, to achieve low loop antenna RF resistance.

An MF loop antenna is normally matching using one of the circuits shown in Figure 3.15. Figure 3.15(a) uses a step-down transformer to match the antenna's $R_{loss}$ to the 50$\Omega$ transmitter output, and a series capacitance to resonate the loop inductance ($L_{ant}$).

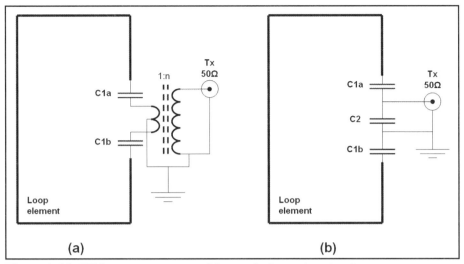

**Figure 3.15: MF loop antenna matching techniques (see text).**

$L_{ant}$ in henries is given approximately by equation (16):

$$Lant = 2 \times 10^{-7} \times P \times \log e \frac{(3440 \times A)}{(d \times P)} \qquad (16)$$

where

P is the overall length of the loop perimeter (m)
A is the loop area (m²)
d is the conductor diameter (mm).

The capacitance required to resonate the arrangement, $C_{tune}$, can be calculated using:

$$Ctune\ (henries) = \frac{1}{4 \times \pi^2 \times fres^2 \times Lant} \qquad [17]$$

Where $f_{res}$ is the antenna's resonant frequency of operation.

$C_{tune}$ is often divided into two the series capacitors as shown in Figure 3.15(a) as C1a and C1b. Dividing $C_{tune}$ in this way allows the loop antenna's voltages to be approximately balanced with respect to ground. Therefore, the value of C1a and C1b is double $C_{tune}$.

The required step-down transformer turns ratio is given by:

$$Turns\ ratio(n) = \sqrt{\left(\frac{Rload}{Rloss}\right)}$$

In this case, $R_{loss}$ is primarily the RF resistance of the loop conductor and this is often around 2Ω for an MF antenna. Taking $R_{load}$ as the transmitter's output impedance of 50Ω allows an estimation of the step-down transformer turns ratio to be made of around 5:1.

An alternative matching arrangement uses a capacitive matching network, as shown in Figure 3.15(b). The values of C1 and C2 are:

$$C1\ (pF) = \frac{1}{2 \times \pi \times \left(2 \times \pi \times f \times Lant - \sqrt{Rloss \times (Rload - Rloss)}\right)} \qquad [18]$$

C1 is often divided into two the series capacitors as shown in Figure 3.15(b) as C1a and C1b. Therefore, the value of C1a and C1b is double C1.

$$C2\ (pF) = \frac{\sqrt{\dfrac{(Rload - Rloss)}{Rloss}}}{2 \times \pi \times f \times Rload} \qquad [19]$$

In a similar manner to a vertical antenna, achieving a good performance from a loop antenna depends primarily on its size. The radiation resistance is proportional to the square of the loop area (A), therefore is advantageous to make the loop as high and long as possible. At 472kHz, a loop antenna should be competitive in efficiency with a vertical (however, at the time of writing, very few loop antennas appear to have been tried on this band).

The main advantage of an MF transmitting loop antenna is that the loop voltages are much lower compared to an MF vertical antenna. This results in lower dielectric losses in objects around the antenna. This makes a loop antenna a good choice for wooded surroundings, where trees close to the antenna could lead to a very poor efficiency of the vertical antenna. This seems to be a common situation in North America, where several loop antennas have been constructed using branches of tall trees to support the loop element. Loop antennas are not dependant on a low resistance ground connection, so there tends to be an improvement where there is very dry or rocky soil compared to using a vertical antenna. A disadvantage is that stronger antenna supports are required to hold the thick loop conductor in position. A further drawback is the directional

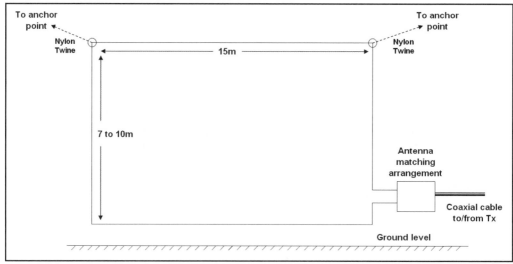

**Figure 3.16: Concept of a rectangular MF loop antenna (based on the antennas used by G3YMC and G3FYX).**

properties of the antenna because the radiated signal will be reduced in some directions due to the nulls in the radiation pattern. Unfortunately, in most domestic locations, options for changing the orientation of a large loop are usually limited.

### 3.11.1 Example Loop Antennas

Figure 3.16 shows the concept of the loop antennas used by Dave Sergeant, G3YMC, and Roy Emery, G3FYX. Both of these antennas are installed in domestic locations in a suburban environment. The dimensions in Figure 3.16 are given as a guide only.

G3YMC's loop antenna was installed in the back garden with dimensions of 15m x 7m, giving an area for the antenna of about 100m². Experimentation with the wire used for the loop resulted in heavy duty loudspeaker cable being used with its pairs connected in parallel. This gave a DC resistance of less than 0.1Ω. One end was supported using a 10m pole by the house, the other end is at only 5m because rear guying of a pole was not possible. The wire is run in the form of a sort of rhombus between these points, with the lower sides running along the garden fence about 0.3m above ground. The loop is fed at one corner at ground level, via a matching box attached to the wall of the house.

G3FYX's loop antenna was also installed in the back garden with dimensions of about 20m x 7m, giving an antenna area of around 140m². Heavy duty copper wire was used for the loop that was suspended between the house and a pole at the end of the garden. The matching arrangement was installed in the shack with the antenna fed at one corner.

### 3.12 An Overview of Loop Antennas used for Reception

Most MF antennas are designed to operate in the electric field of the electromagnetic wave. However, there is an advantage to using an antenna that operates in the magnetic field because a 'magnetic' antenna is much less susceptible to the electric component of nearby interference sources. This is particularly important on the lower-frequency bands. An example of an antenna that operates in the electromagnetic wave's magnetic field is the electrically small loop antenna. These also have the advantage of being relatively small compared to other MF antennas.

Most local noise sources in the MF range are usually caused from common-mode noise currents flowing through mains wiring, giving rise to magnetic fields that a loop antenna is likely to pick up. Consequently, using a loop antenna inside or near a building can often yield poor results on receive. However, these noise source fields rapidly decrease in strength as the antenna is moved away from the offending wiring or noise source. Moving a receiving loop antenna by only a few metres can result in substantial reduction in noise and an improvement in the signal being received. Accordingly, it is important to experiment with different positions when using a receiving loop antenna because often a quiet spot can be found even where high noise levels exist all around.

Receiving loop antennas have a figure-of-eight directional pattern, with nulls at right angles to the plane of the loop and maximum sensitivity along the plane of the loop. This directional null characteristic of a loop antenna

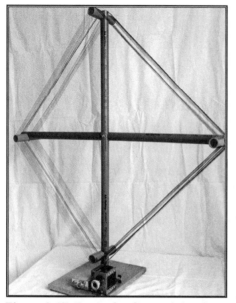

**Figure 3.17: Example of a receiving loop antenna made by PA0SE.**

is often very effective in eliminating distant noise that can arise from various sources. Furthermore, the loop antenna's null can sometimes be used to suppress local noise.

An example of a receiving loop antenna used by PA0SE is shown in Figure 3.17. For the 630m band this consists of about 10 turns of wire wound onto a wooden cross-shaped frame, typically about 1m² in area, tuned by a 500pF variable capacitor. The receiver input is fed via a low impedance single-turn link winding. The output of the loop is small and so a low-noise preamplifier will normally be required, such as the one shown in Figure 3.18. The Q of the loop is typically 100 or more, so re-tuning will be required within the narrow 630m band.

The high Q of a magnetic loop antenna provides an excellent filter in front of a receiver, reducing overload and cross-modulation from adjacent strong signals. Many amateurs have used much larger tuned loops for reception, which achieve higher output signal levels and so can dispense with the preamplifier, at the expense of being physically larger and so more bulky.

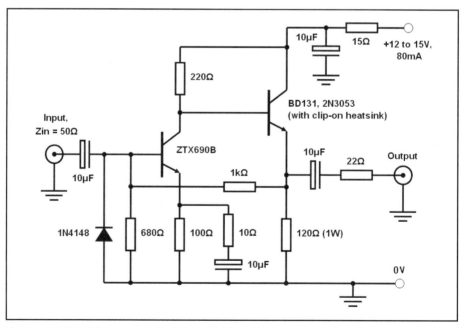

**Figure 3.18: 50Ω preamp circuit suitable for a receiving loop antenna. Gain is about 20dB, noise figure about 3dB.**

# End-Fed Wire Antennas

Within this chapter, end-fed antennas for use on the 160m, 80m and 60m bands are summarised in terms of:

- their design and construction
- introducing feeder cable matching techniques
- earth systems and their implementation.

End-fed antennas for use on the 630m band have not been included in this chapter because their design and construction has been described in Chapter 3.

## 4.1 The End-fed Antenna

The most straightforward of all HF antennas is a length of wire suspended as high as possible between two anchor points, with one end of the wire connected directly to the radio equipment. An example of an end-fed antenna is shown in Figure 4.1 (overleaf). This may seem a rather straightforward antenna, however an end-fed wire can achieve surprisingly good results and can be fairly inconspicuous compared to other types of antenna. When the antenna tends to be longer than a wavelength (λ), it is often referred to as a long wire as well as an end-fed antenna.

With the antenna's wire span secured at each end at height, the radio equipment is connected to the wire span's nearer end using a length of wire run from the Antenna Tuning Unit's (ATU) unbalanced termination. The ATU then provides the mechanism to match the antenna to the transceiver at the operating frequency. The example shown as Figure 4.1 is often referred to as an inverted-L end-fed antenna and is also known as a Marconi antenna.

One of the undesirable aspects of the end-fed wire is that it can present a wide range of impedances at its feed point and many ATUs have difficulty accommodating such a range. However, the choice of end-fed wire's length

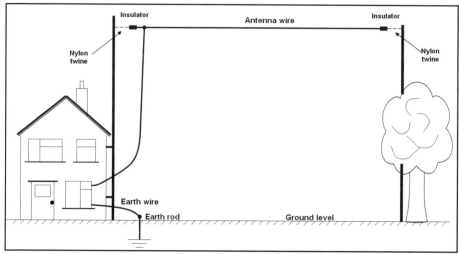

**Figure 4.1: The end-fed antenna, the most straightforward of all multi-band antennas.**

can alleviate some of the matching problems (as discussed later within this chapter). In addition, with the wire being directly connected to the ATU, a significant amount of the transmitted RF power can be radiated in the shack. This could result in various undesirable effects including RF burns and interference to other equipment for example.

## 4.2 Practical HF End-fed Antennas

The length of the wire span determines the lowest band that is practical to use. An eighth wavelength ($\lambda/8$) span of wire is about the minimum practical length usable and tends to present a low impedance at the wire's end. The same length of wire will also work as quarter wavelength ($\lambda/4$) antenna and similarly tends to present a low impedance at its end. However, when the wire is used as a half wavelength ($\lambda/2$) antenna the impedance presented is very high and can result in problems when trying to match the antenna to the transceiver, depending upon the ATU used. Similarly, when the same wire is used as a one wavelength long antenna, then the impedance presented becomes high. Generally, end-fed antennas installed in domestic locations for use on the bands from 160m to 60m tend not to be more than a wavelength ($\lambda$) long because of space limitations.

Guidance for selecting an optimum length for an end-fed wire antenna was described by Alan Chester, G3CCB, based on matching an end-fed wire using a conventional ATU that uses variable inductance/capacitance to tune out the mismatch [13]. Based on G3CCB's work, the shortest practical wire span length for a 160m band end-fed antenna is 21m (ie $\lambda/8$). This wire span then acts as a quarter wave ($\lambda/4$) antenna on the 80m and close to a third wavelength ($\lambda/3$) antenna on the 60m band.

### 4.2.1 Antenna Wire

Wire antennas can be made from any copper wire. The RF resistance of copper wire increases as the diameter of the wire decreases. However, in most types of antennas constructed from wire, the radiation resistance

($R_{rad}$) will be much higher than the conductor's resistance (Rc) allowing the antenna to be an efficient radiator of RF energy. In most cases, the selection of wire for an antenna will be based primarily on its physical properties.

For long wire antennas the preferred material is 14 Standard Wire Gauge (SWG) hard-drawn copper wire and this is ideal for applications where significant stretch cannot be tolerated. Care is required when handling this wire because it has a tendency to spiral when it is unrolled. Make sure that kinks do not develop when handling this type of wire because this wire has a tendency to break (later) at any kink.

However, hard-drawn copper wire has become difficult to acquire in recent times and a suitable alternative is 17A-rated insulated multi-stranded copper wire. This type of wire is produced for the automobile industry, where a tough and reliable cable is required that is able to be for used for prolonged periods in the wet. When using multi-stranded copper wire for an antenna, a good practice is to solder the conductor at each end to help maintain the continuity of the cable. Each soldered joint should then be wrapped in several layers of plumbers' PTFE tape to protect it. Then a length of heatshrink should be shrunk over the joint to weatherproof it. Self-amalgamating tape could also be used.

## 4.3 Remote End-fed Antenna

Situating an end-fed antenna's feed point remotely from the house/building avoids and minimises the undesirable effects associated from RF radiation in the shack. Remotely locating the end-fed antenna's feed point also has the benefit that Electromagnetic Compatibility (EMC) electrical noise problems can be minimised on both transmit and receive. In addition, the unpredictable effect on the antenna caused by possible conduit, wiring and water pipe resonances associated with the house can be reduced. The concept of this arrangement is shown as Figure 4.2.

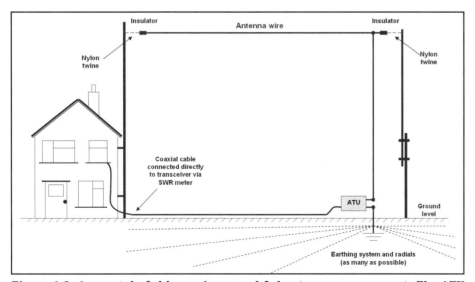

**Figure 4.2: A remotely fed long wire or end-fed antenna arrangement. The ATU can be either preset or automatic and may require a control cable in addition to the coaxial cable feeder.**

A disadvantage of this arrangement is that the ATU is located at a distance from the transceiver. This can be inconvenient when it comes to making adjustments to the ATU, for example when tuning up between bands. An ATU that can be remotely controlled provides a convenient method to overcome this problem of matching the antenna at a distance from the shack. There are a variety of ATUs commercially available from a number of suppliers that tend to be of the auto-tuner type that may be suitable as a remote-ATU. When choosing an ATU for use as a remote-tuner it is important to select one that is capable of handling the SWR range encountered with the station's antenna system for the amateur bands/powers that are intended to be used. A remote ATU will need to be protected from exposure to the weather: situating it inside a shed, or other outbuilding, is ideal. If this is not possible, then a suitable arrangement to protect the remote-ATU from the effects of the weather is required. This might be as simple as an upturned plastic storage box of the type available from supermarkets etc, though you must make sure that any water that gets in can get out again (drill holes in the base, originally the lid) and that it does not deteriorate in ultraviolet light (a coat of paint may help).

## 4.4 Transformer End-fed Antenna Matching

A technique to resolve situations where the impedance presented by an end-fed wire exceeds the ATU's capabilities is to transform the impedance to bring it into the range of most ATUs. A method to do this is to use an unbalanced radio frequency auto-transformer connected between the antenna and the ATU. This arrangement has the advantage that a length of coaxial cable can be run between the ATU and the transformer allowing the antenna's feed point to be remotely located outside, away

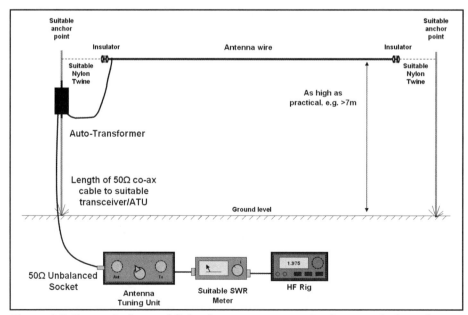

**Figure 4.3: Concept of an end-fed antenna arrangement using an auto-transformer to match the antenna to the feeder.**

from the shack. This arrangement has the advantage of directly avoiding high RF powers from being radiated within the shack, so preventing any undesirable effects that this may cause. The concept of this arrangement is shown in Figure 4.3.

This arrangement should be worked against a good RF earthing system (as shown in Figures 4.1 and 4.2). However, in Figure 4.3 the earthing arrangements have not been shown for clarity.

### 4.4.1 The Unun transformer

Transformers using iron powder toroid cores can be constructed to cover frequency ranges from about 2 to 40MHz. To enable the transformer to work efficiently, it is important that the wires forming the windings are laid side-by-side to maximise the magnetic field coupling between them. There will always be some leakage inductance associated with a transformer and this increases in proportion to the transformer's self-inductance. Therefore, a transformer that works well at 1.81MHz may not work as well as the frequency increases and this often shows as a worsening SWR.

The concept of a 9:1 and a 4:1 impedance transforming ratio unbalanced-to-unbalanced auto-transformer (or unun) is shown in Figure 4.4. If the end-fed wire is thought of as being connected to the auto-transformer's secondary winding, then the ATU's unbalanced 'antenna' socket is connected to the auto-transformer's primary winding. The antenna's impedance presented at the auto-transformer's secondary winding is transformed down to present a lower impedance at the primary winding,

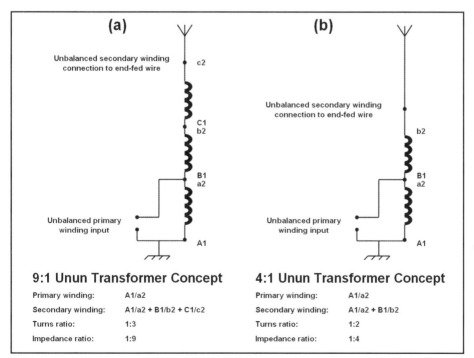

Figure 4.4: Concept of 9:1 (a) and 4:1 (b) unbalanced to unbalanced (unun) transformers.

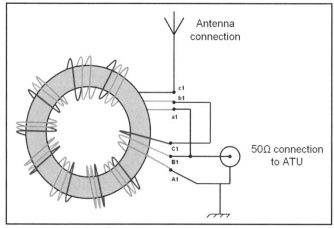

**Figure 4.5: Unun 9:1 transformer connection details.**

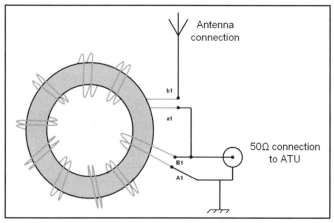

**Figure 4.6: Unun 4:1 transformer connection details.**

enabling it to be brought within the capabilities of most ATUs.

Peter Miles, VK6YSF, and John Parfrey, M0UKD, have published several toroid iron powder core unun 9:1 and 4:1 impedance ratio auto-transformer designs for use with end-fed wire antennas, with details made available online [14] [15]. There are several types of toroidal core that can be used for an unun to match an end-fed antenna for use between 1.8MHz to 5.4MHz. However, a T200-2 Micrometals iron powder toroid works well. These toroidal cores are obtainable from some radio rally traders, radio component retailers and online suppliers.

A 9:1 impedance ratio auto-transformer can be made by winding 18 trifilar 3-wire turns on to a T200-2 core. A lower 4:1 impedance ratio transformer can be made using a T200-2 core in a similar manner using 18 bifilar wound 2-wire turns. Figure 4.5 and Figure 4.6 summarise the connection arrangements for these transformers. A T200-2 based transformer can handle transmit powers of over 100W. If higher power transmit powers are to be used, then two T200-2 cores can be stacked to improve the power handling capabilities. A smaller diameter T130-2 core could be used, however its power handling capabilities are lower compared to a T200-2 core.

### 4.4.2 Example of 9:1 in use

Figure 4.7 illustrates an example of a 9:1 impedance ratio transformer using two stacked Micrometals Iron Powder Toroid T130-2 cores that was used to match an end-fed wire covering the 160m to 60m bands. The antenna had a wire span of 21m and this was mounted at a height of around 7m above the ground and the setup was similar to that shown in Figure 4.3. This transformer comprised 9 trifilar wound 3-wire turns with a small gap left between each turn as shown. Figure 4.7 shows where the connection of the coaxial cable was made to the primary winding with the secondary winding's connection to the antenna.

This transformer arrangement allowed RF powers of up to 100W to be handled using an ATU to provide a good match to the transceiver. This end-fed antenna was worked against an artificial earthing system and this technique is described later within this chapter. The arrangement enabled many contacts to be made across the UK, Europe and outside.

## 4.5 Earthing Techniques

For some antenna designs to operate efficiently a good RF earth is often required. The end-fed wire antenna is a good example of where an RF earth can potentially improve the performance of the antenna.

### 4.5.1 Using Real Earth

In practice a good RF earth connection is difficult to find and is only practicable from a ground floor room. The problem with the 'earth stake' is that the ground has resistance and the cable connecting the earth stake to the radio has reactance. Many ways have been tried to reduce the ground resistance and, in general, the more copper that can be buried in the ground the better. An RF earth can be made using about $60m^2$ of galvanised chicken wire or the somewhat thicker welded galvanized mesh of typically 25mm squares. This is laid on the lawn early in the year. Cut the grass short, then lay out the chicken wire or mesh. Peg it down with large staples made from hard-drawn copper wire or cheap metal tent pegs. The grass will grow up through the chicken wire netting and the wire will tend to disappear into the ground over a period of about two months. In the early stages, the lawn has to be mown carefully, a little higher than usual, so that the lawnmower does not cut too close and chew up the carefully laid wire netting (and in so doing, potentially damaging the lawnmower).

Figure 4.7: Example of a 9:1 unun auto-transformer using two stacked T130-2 toroidal cores used to match a 160m to 60m band end-fed wire.

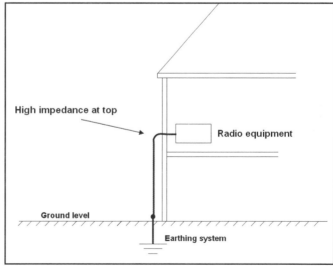

Figure 4.8: Concept of why RF ground cable runs from upper floors can be ineffective. A ground cable run with quarter-wavelength resonance (or odd multiple) is ineffective because very little current flows into it.

Low band 'DX' operators tend to use multiple radials, where many wires are buried that radiate out from the earth connection. The rule seems to be the more wires the better. These types of direct connection to earth arrangements can also provide an electrical safety earth to the radio equipment in the shack.

When the shack is located above the first floor as shown in Figure 4.8, engineering a low-impedance earth connection to ground level can become difficult using the methods described. This is because the length of the cable used to connect the radio equipment to the earth system could become a significant fraction of a wavelength (depending upon the band in use). At frequencies where the earth cable's length is close to one or three quarters of a wavelength, the earth connection will present a high impedance at RF frequencies. Effectively, the earth connection acts like an RF insulator and this is opposite to that required. This situation could happen on one or more of the amateur lower HF bands depending upon the length of the cable used. The earth cable used to connect the earth system to the radio equipment should be of the heavier duty type (eg 4 to 6mm$^2$, or larger, insulated stranded copper cable) to give a low dc resistance and be kept as short as is practical.

Another technique of obtaining a good RF earth is to connect a quarter-wave ($\lambda/4$) radial for each band to the transceiver and ATU earth connector, running the free ends outside away from the transceiver. The impedance at the end of the radial is high and the current will be low, conversely where the radial is connected to the radio equipment its impedance will be low and the RF potential close to zero. The problem is then where to locate each radial for each band to be used. This arrangement will require some experimenting to find the best position, however the radials can be bent or even

---

**WARNING: Protective Multiple Earthing (PME)**

Many houses in the UK are wired on what is known as the PME system. In this system the earth conductor of the consumer's installation is bonded to the neutral close to where the supply enters the premises and there is no separate earth conductor going back to the sub-station. Under certain rare supply fault conditions a shock or fire risk could occur where external conductors such as antennas or earths are connected. For this reason the supply regulations require additional bonding and similar precautions in PME systems.

Many houses in UK were wired on the old TN-S system, where a separate earth goes back to the sub-station. In such systems there were no problems with connecting an external radio antenna or earth. It has recently become evident that changes to maintenance and installation practice mean that the inherent safety of the old TNS systems cannot always be guaranteed. The situation is being reviewed. **Until further information is available all installations should be treated as if they were PME.** Note that PME is also designated as TN-CS by the IET Wiring Regulations BS 7671, which follows the appropriate IET documents.

Read the RSGB leaflet EMC 07 Earthing and the Radio Amateur [8] before connecting any earth or antenna system to equipment inside the house. The leaflet is available free from the RSGB EMC Committee website or on request from RSGB HQ.

**If in doubt consult a qualified electrician.**

You should also check to see whether Building Control must be informed before starting any work.

---

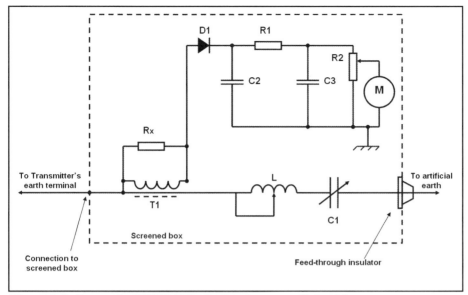

**Figure 4.9: Concept of SM6AQR's design for an earth lead tuner.**

folded, although the length may have to be altered to maintain resonance. The radials are best located outside the buildig and run in the horizontal plane to minimise any coupling with the domestic electrical wiring. The best way to check the resonance of a radial is to connect it to the radio earth, make a loop in the radial and use a dip meter to check its resonance. If such an instrument is unavailable then use an RF current meter and adjust the radial length for maximum current.

### 4.5.2 Artificial Earths

Alternatively, one single radial can be tuned on any band to place a zero RF potential at the transceiver/ATU by inserting a LC series tuning circuit between the transceiver/ATU and the radial. These units are commercially available and have a tuneable LC tuning circuit. These units often have a through-current RF indicator to help tuning the radial or earth lead to resonance (maximum current).

A unit could also be made and an example designed by SM6AQR [16] is shown in Figure 4.9. See also Table 4.1. This design used a 28µH 'roller-coaster' inductor and a 200-300pF air spaced tuning capacitor with a plate spacing of at least 1mm. The capacitor and its shaft must be insulated from the metal cabinet used to house the circuitry. Alternatively, a multi-tapped fixed coil comprising as many taps as possible could be used as the inductor. The tuning indicator consists of a current transformer, rectifier, smoothing filter, sensitivity potentiometer and DC microammeter. The 'primary' of the current transformer is the artificial earth lead and this passes through the centre of the T1 ferrite toroid core. Onto this core the secondary was wound using 20 turns of thin enamelled wire. The resistor Rx across the T1 secondary should be non-inductive and be between 22 and 100Ω. Resistor Rx is selected to enable a convenient meter deflection to be set with the sensitivity control R2 on each required frequency and for the RF power used.

Caution: A separate electrical safety earth should always be used, in addition to the RF earth described above.

### 4.6 Radiation Pattern

Figure 4.10 shows the predicted radiation patterns in the horizontal and vertical planes using the MMANA-GAL antenna analysis application [7] for a 21m long end-fed wire antenna horizontally installed at 15m agl. These radiation patterns are predicted for operation on the 160m, 80m and 60m bands where the end-fed wire antenna is close to $\lambda/8$, $\lambda/4$ and $\lambda/3$ in length respectively.

The predicted horizontal radiation pattern is very similar for 160m, 80m and 60m with little difference between the curves. The horizontal radiation is close to omnidirectional, however the curves indicate an increase of around 3dB in the radiation broadside of the antenna. The vertical radiation patterns for 160m and 80m are very similar with much of the radiation directed skywards. On the 60m band, the vertical radiation pattern is similar although slightly less radiation is directed skywards. This makes the antenna suited to more localised skip allowing contacts to be made up to around 800km to 1200km on the 160m, 80m and 60m bands. However, depending upon the propagation conditions the antenna does enable more distant stations to be worked because some radiation is directed at a lower angle towards the horizon.

The predicted radiation patterns for this end-fed wire antenna provide a general guide to the performance of this type of antenna when operated on the 160m, 80m or 60m bands. However, the performance of an end-fed wire of a much longer length and installed at a greater height can be expected to show an improvement over the antenna used in the prediction.

| Components | Item | Description |
|---|---|---|
| Toroid core | T1 | Amidon T50-43 ferrite toroid core. The transformer's primary is simply the earth lead through the toroid centre. The secondary = 20t small gauge enamelled wire. |
| Variable inductor | L | 28µH roller-coaster or multi-tapped coil with 10-position switch as described in the text. |
| Variable capacitor | C1 | 200pF or more air-spaced variable capacitor with >1mm spacing that is insulated from panel and case. |
| Diode | D1 | AA119 |
| Resistors | R1 | 1kΩ |
| | R2 | 10kΩ potentiometer. |
| | Rx | For value, see text. |
| Moving coil meter | M | 100µA FSD or less. |

Table 4.1: Summary of the components used in SM6AQR's artificial earth circuit shown in Figure 4.9.

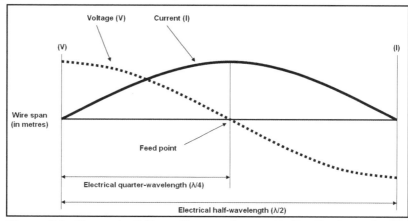

# 5

# Dipole Wire Antennas

Within this chapter, dipole antennas for use on the 160m, 80m and 60m bands are summarised in terms of their:
- design and construction
- radiation patterns
- installation techniques.

## 5.1 The Centre-fed Dipole

A centrally fed electrically half wavelength dipole has a feed point that coincides where the voltage is at a minimum and the current is at a maximum. This relationship, between the voltage and current, results in a feed point impedance of around 50 to 70Ω. The actual feed point impedance is influenced by the height of the antenna above the ground, by any close objects and, to some extent, by the gauge of the wire used [17]. The current and voltage distributions in one dipole leg are matched by those in the opposite leg as shown in Figure 5.1. This means that the half wavelength dipole is a balanced single band antenna that can be directly fed using a balanced feeder run from the radio equip-

**Figure 5.1: Concept of the voltage and current distributions along a half-wave (λ/2) dipole. The feeder cable is connected to the centre of the antenna where the feed impedance is low**

ment. The antenna can be readily connected to a 50Ω feeder cable, giving a low SWR. However, if an unbalanced 50Ω coaxial feeder cable is directly connected to the feed point, then good practice is to use a balanced-to-unbalanced (balun) transition to avoid the effects that arise from common mode currents (see Chapter 8). In most cases, the dipole has an efficiency that exceeds 95%, making it an effective antenna that is practical to construct.

The physical length of a λ/2 long antenna can be calculated using equation (1) (see Chapter 2):

$$\text{Length}(m) = \frac{150(n-0.05)}{f} \qquad [1]$$

Where n is the number of complete half-waves in the antenna and f is the frequency in megahertz (MHz). As outlined previously, this equation allows for several factors that slow the velocity of the wave along the wire span that affect the length of the antenna for true resonance.

Therefore, for a practical horizontally installed λ/2 antenna (where n = 1), its physical length can be calculated using equation (2) (see Chapter 2):

$$\text{Length}(m) = \frac{150 \times (0.95)}{f} \qquad [2]$$

Table 5.1 summarises dipole lengths for use on the 160m, 80m and 60m bands for reference.

It should be noted that equation (1) gives the total dipole length and the wire has to be cut in half at the centre, giving two legs of λ/4 each, where the feeder cable is connected. The gap between the two legs also forms part of the whole dipole length.

### 5.2 Radiation Pattern

The radiation pattern usually shown for a dipole is the familiar free space azimuth polar 'figure of eight' diagram where there are clear nulls at the ends of the dipole's legs (as previously shown in Figure 2.3). However, at a domestic location, dipoles used on 160m, 80m or 60m tend to be installed at

| Band | Frequency (MHz) | Dipole length (m) | Wire diameter (mm) |
|------|------|------|------|
| 160m | 1.8250 | 78.1 | |
| | 1.8500 | 77.0 | 1 to 2 |
| | 1.9500 | 73.1 | |
| 80m | 3.5500 | 40.1 | |
| | 3.6500 | 39.0 | 1 to 2 |
| | 3.7500 | 38.0 | |
| 60m | 5.2620 | 27.1 | |
| | 5.3200 | 26.8 | 1 to 2 |
| | 5.3715 | 26.5 | |
| | 5.4035 | 26.4 | |

**Table 5.1: Dipole dimension details for the 160m to 60m bands.**

a height that is a fraction of their operational wavelength. The ground below the antenna produces reflections that modify the actual radiation pattern of the antenna. Figure 5.2 shows the predicted radiation patterns in the

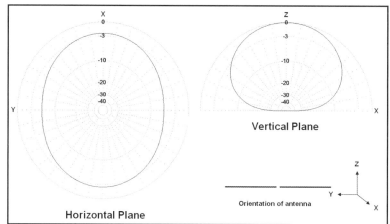

Figure 5.2: MMANA-GAL predicted horizontal and vertical plane radiation patterns for a 160m dipole at 15m agl. The predicted radiation patterns for 80m and 60m dipole antennas at 15m agl do not significantly differ from the 160m dipole's radiation pattern.

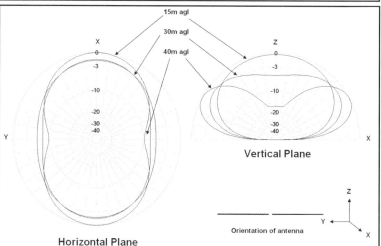

Figure 5.3: MMANA-GAL predicted horizontal and vertical plane radiation patterns for a 80m dipole at 15m, 30 and 40m agl. As the antenna's height increases, so the vertical plane radiation pattern modifies.

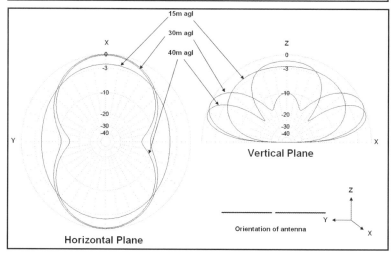

Figure 5.4: MMANA-GAL predicted horizontal and vertical plane radiation patterns for a 60m dipole at 15m, 30 and 40m agl. As the antenna's height increases, so the vertical plane radiation pattern tends to have more radiation directed at a lower angle.

horizontal and vertical planes for a 160m dipole centred on 1.85MHz. This radiation pattern was predicted for the antenna using MMANA-GAL [7] with the antenna at 15m agl. The horizontal plane radiation pattern shows that there is some directivity either side of the wire span. However, unlike the free space pattern, there are no nulls at the antenna's end. The vertical plane indicates that much of the radiation is directed skywards with nominal radiated towards the horizon. If the antenna is raised to 30m agl, the radiation pattern still does not significantly differ from that at 15m agl. This makes the antenna suited to more localised skip enabling contacts to be made up to around 800km. However depending upon the propagation conditions the antenna does enable more distant stations to be worked because some radiation is directed at a lower angle towards the horizon. When installed at 15m agl, the predicted radiation patterns for 80m and 60m dipole antennas do not significantly differ from that shown in Figure 5.2 for the 160m dipole's radiation pattern.

Figure 5.3 shows the predicted radiation patterns in the horizontal and vertical planes for a 80m dipole centred on 3.65MHz. The radiation patterns are predicted with the antenna at 15m, 30m and 45m agl for comparison. On the 80m band, the antenna's height starts to become significant compared to the wavelength of operation. As the height of the antenna increases, then both the horizontal and vertical radiation patterns change. The horizontal radiation pattern starts to show nulls developing at the wire span ends as the antenna's height in increased. More radiation is directed away either side of the wire span improving the directivity of the antenna. However, the vertical radiation pattern shows that as the antenna's height is increased, then more radiation is directed at a lower angle towards the horizon. With the antenna at 15m agl, much of the radiation is directed skywards and this makes the antenna suited to more localised skip enabling contacts up to around 800km to be made. However, as the antenna's height is raised, more radiation is directed towards the horizon enabling more distant stations to be worked provided the propagation conditions are suitable.

Figure 5.4 shows the predicted radiation patterns in the horizontal and vertical planes for a 60m dipole centred on 5.32MHz. These radiation patterns were predicted with the antenna at 15m, 30m and 45m agl for comparison. On the 60m band, the antenna's height becomes even more significant compared to the wavelength of operation. As the height of the antenna increases, then both the horizontal and vertical radiation patterns change in a similar way as shown for the 80m dipole. At 30m and 40m agl, the horizontal radiation pattern shows larger nulls developing at the wire span ends with radiation directed away either side of the wire span giving improved the directivity. However, the vertical radiation pattern shows that as the antenna's height is increased, then more radiation is directed at an even lower angle towards the horizon compared to the 80m dipole. With the antenna at 15m agl, this makes the antenna suited to more localised skip allowing contacts to be made up to around 800 to 1200km. However, as the antenna's height is raised to 30m agl, more radiation is directed towards the horizon enabling more distant stations to be worked provided the propagation conditions are suitable. The vertical radiation pattern with the antenna at 40m agl shows significant radiation directed skywards and towards the horizon making the antenna suited to working both local and more distant stations.

## 5.3 The Inverted-V Dipole

The dipole antenna normally requires two supports and this may be a problem at some locations. The solution may be to mount the antenna so that it is vertical or sloping. Where the space to install the antenna is restricted, the dipole's elements can be arranged in an inverted "V" configuration. An inverted-V dipole has its two wire legs sloping down towards the ground from the central feed point, typically creating around a 120° angle between the legs of the dipole. This arrangement has the advantage that only a single support is required to hold up the central feed point, with this usually mounted at the top of a mast or pole. This configuration of dipole can considerably reduce the ground footprint of the antenna without significantly impacting on its performance. In addition, the height of the feed point influences the performance of the antenna and this arrangement allows the feed point to be situated as high above the ground as possible.

When viewed from the side, the antenna looks like the letter "V" turned upside down: this is where it gets its name. Figure 5.5 illustrates the concept of an inverted-V dipole for reference. When a metal mast is used to support the antenna, the feed point needs to be isolated from the mast to avoid it impairing the performance of the antenna through induction. One method to isolate the feed point is to attach a length of plastic tube to the top of the mast with about 15 to 30cm of the tube protruding above it. The feed point can then be fastened to the top of this tube giving at least 100mm of clearance. When the dipole is fed with a balanced feeder cable, a metal mast can also affect the feeder cable through induction and so impair the performance of the antenna. There should be a gap left of at least 25mm (ideally more) to isolate the balanced feeder cable from the mast to avoid this effect.

Figure 5.6 (overleaf) shows the predicted horizontal and vertical radiation patterns for a 80m inverted V dipole centred on 3.65MHz. The feed point was at 15m agl, while the dipole's ends were situated at 10m agl, giving an angle between the dipole's legs of around 150°. The inverted V

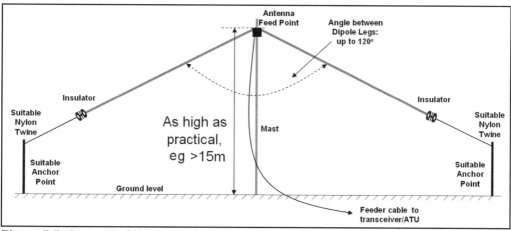

**Figure 5.5: Concept of the inverted-V dipole antenna.**

**Figure 5.6:**
**MMANA-GAL predict-**
**ed radiation patterns**
**for an 80m inverted**
**V dipole with its feed**
**point at 15m agl and**
**each end at 10m agl.**

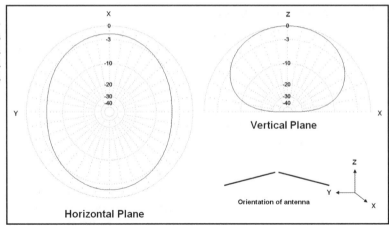

dipole's vertical and horizontal radiation patterns are very similar to those predicted when the dipole's wire span is run horizontally straight above the ground. This indicates that an inverted V dipole's performance is very similar to the conventionally run dipole. The radiation patterns shown in Figure 5.6 are very similar for a 160m or 60m dipole when installed with their feed point at 15m agl and wire ends at 10m agl.

Another method to fit a dipole into the space available is to equally bend over the ends of a dipole's legs for a short length up to about 15%. This should not significantly affect the performance of the antenna provided the configuration of the dipole is kept symmetrical.

## 5.4 Construction and Installation

The usual practice to install a dipole is to suspend the antenna between two high points with its feeder cable run vertically straight downwards from the feed point as shown in Figure 5.7. Keeping the arrangement as symmetrical as practical tends to maintain the balance of the antenna improving its radiation pattern and helps to minimise undesirable common mode currents.

Dipoles for 160m 80m and 60m are long and, if possible, should be made of hard drawn copper wire to reduce stretching and sagging due to

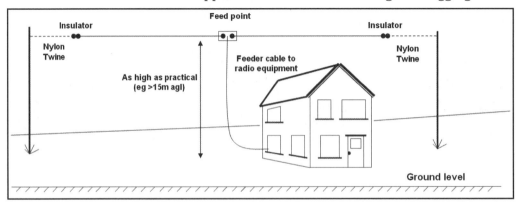

**Figure 5.7: Concept of a dipole installed at a domestic location for the 160m, 80m and 60m bands.**

the weight of the antenna and the feeder cable. If hard drawn copper wire is not available, 17A stranded insulated copper cable could be used and good practice is to solder the ends of the wire to ensure electrical continuity. This type of cable is used by the automobile industry and it is designed for external use (see also Section 4.2.1). Cable suitable for antenna wire can be sourced from amateur radio suppliers, radio rallies or online.

**Figure 5.8: A typical dog-bone dipole centre used for wire antennas.**

The feed point impedance of a dipole at resonance can vary either side of the nominal 73Ω, depending on the antenna's height above ground, the proximity of buildings and any electromagnetic obstacles, together with any bends in the wire. As a result of this, for a practical antenna, it is difficult to obtain an SWR of 1:1 when the antenna is fed with 50Ω coaxial cable. The arrangement used to connect the feeder cable to each leg of the dipole antenna is often suspended within the antenna's span and necessitates a physically strong but lightweight design. Commercially, there are various designs available and a typical dog-bone type dipole centre that was acquired at a radio rally is illustrated in Figure 5.8. This type of dipole centre can be obtained from various suppliers and there are several variations available. Essentially, the dog-bone dipole centre has a hole at each end through which each wire leg of the dipole is firmly attached, usually by tying the wire. A short length of the wire is left protruding so that a ring terminal can be soldered to the wire's end after removal of the insulation. The feeder cable's conductors are then soldered to the other two ring terminals allowing the feeder cable to be connected to each wire leg using the nuts and bolts.

A dipole centre can be made from a sheet of 3mm thick uPVC (unplasticised polyvinyl chloride) as shown in Figure 5.9(a). This design has three holes drilled along the upper section of the dipole centre either side

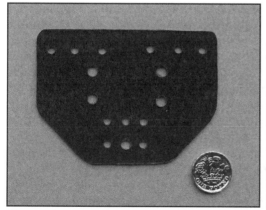

**Figure 5.9(a): A dipole centre used for wire antennas made from a sheet of uPVC.**

**Figure 5.9(b): The dipole centre in use in a dipole fed with 50Ω coaxial cable (balun not shown).**

**Figure 5.10: Dipole wire end termination using a dog bone insulator.**

of the middle as shown. These holes are used to hold in place each wire leg of the dipole by lacing the wire through the holes as shown. Four equally-spaced holes were drilled into the lower section of the dipole centre to hold the feeder cable in place using cable ties that were passed through the holes, over the feeder cable and then tightened. The two larger diameter holes drilled symmetrically either side above where the feeder cable is attached allow the antenna to be installed as an inverted-V if necessary. A short length of heatshrink was passed over each dipole leg and the leg soldered to one of the feeder cable's conductors. After soldering, the joint was protected by wrapping PTFE plumbers' tape around it. Then the heatshrink was slid over each joint and shrunk using a heat-gun to help weatherproof the joint. A larger diameter length of heatshrink was then passed and shrunk over the assembly to project the joints.

The feeder cable was passed over the top of the dipole centre so that the end of the feeder cable points downwards to minimise entry of moisture into the joint. An example of this arrangement is shown in Figure 5.9(b) for an HF antenna where the feeder cable was 50Ω coaxial cable. This antenna used a choke balun formed from several loops of the cable located just under the dipole centre to avoid the effects that arise from common mode currents (see Chapter 8). This dipole centre design allowed the HF antenna's wire span to be suspended horizontally and run as straight as possible. Alternatively, the dipole centre could be fastened to the top of an insulated mast and the antenna installed in an inverted-V configuration with the feeder cable brought downwards. The choice of uPVC for the dipole centre was chosen because this material is designed for use outside in the wet, is fairly rugged and is able to generally withstand degradation from sunlight.

The dipole can be supported using 2mm or 3mm diameter nylon twine with 'dog bone' insulators at the ends of the dipole's legs. When measuring up the wire for each dipole leg, an extra length of about 150mm should be added at each end to give an allowance for connecting the dipole leg to the centre insulator and the end insulator. If each wire end is threaded through the insulator to form a loop, then this allows the length of each dipole leg to be adjusted for minimum SWR by folding the wire back on itself. However, it is important that the dipole is kept symmetrical during this procedure. The wire ends can be temporally held in position using tape and once the optimum length has been determined, cable ties can be used to secure each wire end in place. This method of connecting the dipole's legs to the insulators is shown in Figure 5.10. It is recommended not to use egg insulators and wire as the dipole's leg end supports because this can increase the end-capacitance, causing the antenna's performance to be unpredictable.

# 6

# Multi-Band Wire Antennas

Operating a station on several bands often involves installing a number of antennas, each with its own feeder cable. This can result in several feeder cables being run in parallel and their combined weight may become a problem, eg when raising/lowering the mast. Within this chapter, antenna designs are summarised to enable multiple-band operation using one feeder cable, including the:

- G5RV antenna with and without loading coils
- multi-band doublet using tuned lines
- multi-band doublet with an ATU
- off-centre fed dipole
- magnetic loop antennas.

Most multi-band systems can be improved by using an Antenna Tuning Unit (ATU). Therefore, it is probably a good decision to either purchase or to build an ATU. Most ATU designs are generally based on using straightforward RF circuitry and this technology tends not to date. The constructions of several ATU designs have been included within Chapter 8 (Overview of Matching and Antenna Tuning Techniques).

The half wavelength dipole also presents a low feed point impedance on its third harmonic. This characteristic means the antenna could be used as a third-harmonic antenna enabling operation on two bands. Unfortunately, there is no exact third harmonic relationship between the 160m, 80m and 60m bands. However, a dipole designed to operate on 1.82MHz is close to resonance at around 5.46MHz and could provide a solution for operating on the upper segments of the 60m band. Although, in most cases, an ATU may be required to tune the antenna to obtain a good match, effectively making the antenna operate more like a doublet.

## 6.1 The G5RV Antenna

The G5RV antenna [18] remains a popular HF bands antenna widely used by radio amateurs around the globe. This antenna was devised by Louis Varney, G5RV, around 1946 when he was looking for a solution to getting his station back on the air following the restoration of amateur transmitting licenses in the UK. One of Louis' interests was operating on 20m and his design was based on this requirement. However, the original 31.1m long antenna was found to be effective on the other HF bands, giving a multi-band antenna capable of use from 80m to 10m. The G5RV design is really only resonant at its design frequency. Often, the antenna is considered as acting more like a doublet-type antenna when not used on its resonant band.

The G5RV antenna was devised to work with older valve based radio equipment using a Pi-network as a means of matching the radio equipment to the antenna. The impedances presented by the antenna can result in fairly high SWRs being encountered depending upon the HF band in use. Therefore, an ATU is necessary to allow the antenna to be matched to solid-state transceivers that otherwise would not be able to tolerate the range of SWR met (see also Chapter 8).

### 6.1.1 G5RV Antenna for use on 160m, 80m and 60m Bands

The G5RV design is based on a wire span that is three electrical half wavelengths ($3\lambda/2$) long at a desired frequency, centrally fed by a balanced twin-wire feeder cable that is half an electrical wavelength ($\lambda/2$) long at the same frequency [18]. The length of the wire span (allowing for the velocity factor) is given by:

$$\text{Length of wire span }(m) = \frac{150 \times (n - 0.05)}{f(MHz)} \qquad [20]$$

To use a G5RV to cover the 160m, 80m and 60m bands, three half-waves need to be accommodated along the wire span on the 40m band (7.0 to 7.2MHz). This means that the antenna could also be used on the 40m band and above, although the use of the antenna on the higher bands is not within the scope of this chapter.

Therefore using equation (20), where f = 7.2MHz and n = 3 half wavelengths:

$$\text{Length of wire span }(m) = \frac{150 \times (3 - 0.05)}{7.2(MHz)} = 61.46m$$

In the interests of keeping things straightforward and since the whole system is brought into resonance using an Aerial Tuning Unit (ATU), the antenna's wire span is cut to 61.5m.

The length of the balanced air-spaced twin-wire feeder cable feeder at 7.1MHz (using a 0.98 velocity factor) is given by:

$$\text{Half wavelength feeder }(m) = (0.98) \times \left(\frac{150}{7.2MHz}\right) = 20.42m \qquad [21]$$

The balanced two-wire feeder cable can be open-wire or ladder-line cable and has the advantage that it is low loss. If ladder-line is used, this can be either the 300Ω or 450Ω varieties.

The concept of the 160m version of the G5RV antenna for use on the 160m, 80m and 60m bands is shown in Figure 6.1. Although this antenna may be too long for many domestic locations, this antenna is shorter by about 16m than a dipole cut for 160m and that may help with accommodating this antenna in the space available.

The wire-span's centre impedance at 7.2MHz is about 100Ω and the half wavelength ladder-line acts as a 1:1 impedance transformer presenting this impedance at its end. Therefore, if a 50Ω feeder cable is connected to the ladder-line there will be a mismatch, however this will be low at about 2:1 and be within the tuning capabilities of the ATU enabling a good match to be seen by the transceiver. However, at other frequencies of operation the impedance seen at the end of the ladder-line can vary significantly and to tune the antenna to resonance requires an ATU capable of handling the wide range of impedances that can be encountered.

Connecting an unbalanced coaxial cable to the end of the balanced ladder-line will require an arrangement to minimise common mode currents that flow on the outer of the coaxial cable's screen conductor. There are several balanced-unbalanced techniques available to overcome common mode current problems using a choke balun. However, one uncomplicated method is to make a current choke from about ten 300mm diameter loops of the coaxial cable (held together with cable-ties) and located this close to the coaxial cable's connection with the balanced ladder-line as possible (see also Chapter 8).

On the 160m band, each half of the antenna's horizontal wire span along with around 10.4m of the upper section of the balanced ladder-line cable form a foreshortened λ/2 dipole. The remaining lower section of the ladder-line feeder introduces an unavoidable reactance necessitating the use of an ATU to bring the antenna to resonance.

On the 80m band, each half of the horizontal wire span along with around 9.7m of the upper section of the balanced ladder-line cable now act as a partially folded up 'two half-waves in phase' antenna. In a similar manner to the above, the

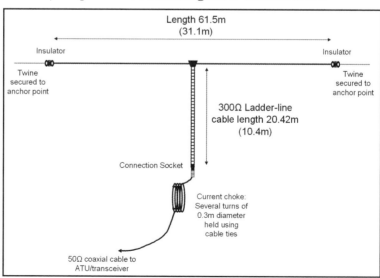

**Figure 6.1: Concept of a 160m G5RV antenna version for use on the 160m, 80m and 60m bands. The dimensions shown bracketed are for the shorter 80m and 60m version of the antenna.**

remaining lower section of the ladder-line feeder introduces an unavoidable reactance necessitating the use of an ATU to bring the antenna to resonance.

On the 60m band, the antenna can be thought of as acting as a 'two-half-waves-in-phase' collinear array. A reactive load is presented at the base of the ladder-line necessitating the use of an ATU to bring the antenna to resonance.

### 6.1.2 G5RV Antenna for the 80m and 60m Bands

The calculations for the 80m version of the G5RV antenna for use on the 80m and 60m bands are similar to the larger version outlined above. However, using a frequency of 14.15MHz gives a wire-span of 31.1m in length with an air-spaced ladder-line of 10.4m long. This gives an antenna that is shorter than a dipole cut for 80m by about 9m, enabling the antenna to be accommodated into a slightly smaller location. The dimensions for the 80m G5RV version of the antenna are shown in brackets in Figure 6.1. The resonant frequency of this antenna is around 14.15MHz. Therefore, this antenna could also be used on the 40m band and above, although the use of the antenna on the higher bands is not within the scope of this chapter. It is this 31.1m long configuration of G5RV antenna is often encountered and is often referred to as a 'full-size' G5RV.

On the 80m band, each half of the horizontal wire span along with around 5.2m of the upper section of the balanced ladder-line cable form a foreshortened $\lambda/2$ dipole. The remaining lower section of the ladder-line feeder introduces an unavoidable reactance, necessitating the use of an ATU to match the antenna.

On the 60m band, the antenna operates in a similar manner to operation on the 80m band. However, the wire-span's length is about 10% longer than a $\lambda/2$ dipole cut for use on the 60m band. Consequently, the antenna will tend to present a high SWR band, again necessitating the use of an ATU to match the antenna.

**Figure 6.2: Predicted radiation patterns for the 160m version of the G5RV antenna on 160m, 80m and 60m with the wire span at 21m agl.**

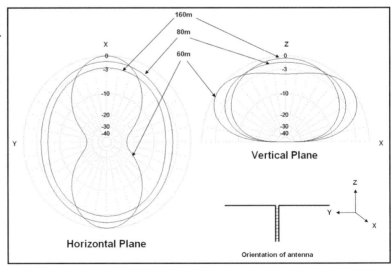

### 6.1.3 G5RV Antenna's Ladder-Line Feeder Length

For both the G5RV antennas described, the ladder-line feeder may have a shorter length if other types of balanced line feeders are used because their velocity factors will be different compared to an air-spaced ladder-line. For example, often the length of the balanced line can reduce to typically 18.6m for the 160m G5RV version and 9.3m for the 80m G5RV version when other types of balanced line are used (eg commercially available polythene insulated 300Ω ladder-line).

### 6.1.4 Radiation Pattern

Figure 6.2 shows the predicted radiation patterns in the horizontal and vertical planes for the 160m version of the G5RV antenna using the MMANA-GAL antenna analysis application [7]. These radiation patterns are predicted for the 160m, 80m and 60m bands with the antenna at 21m agl. On the 160m and 80m bands, the horizontal radiation patterns are very similar, although the performance on 80m has a slight improvement compared to that on 160m. However, on the 60m band, the horizontal radiation pattern takes on more of the form of a dipole with radiation directed away either side of the wire span, giving improved directivity on this band. The vertical radiation pattern for 160m and 80m are very similar, with much of the radiation directed skywards. This makes the antenna suited to more localised skip, allowing contacts to be made up to around 800km on the 160m and 80m bands. However, depending upon the propagation conditions the antenna does enable more distant stations to be worked on 160m and 80m because some radiation is directed at a lower angle towards the horizon. On the 60m band, the vertical radiation pattern is directed at a lower angle towards the horizon compared to 160m and 80m. This enables more distant stations to be worked provided the propagation conditions are suitable on the 60m band.

The radiation patterns in the horizontal and vertical planes for the 80m version of the G5RV antenna were also predicted using the MMANA-GAL application [7]. The radiation patterns on 80m and 60m bands were modelled with the antenna at 11m agl and were very similar to those predicted for the larger 160m version of the G5RV antenna when operated on 160m and a similar performance can be expected.

### 6.1.5 G5RV Antenna Inverted-V and Double-L Variations

The G5RV antenna's geometry can be altered by converting it into an inverted-V or by bending the ends down forming a double-L configuration to enable the antenna to be fitted into a smaller space without modification to the length. The same guidance can be applied to installing a G5RV as an inverted-V antenna as described for the dipole antenna in Section 5.3 (see Figure 5.5).

The inverted-V configuration of the antenna has a radiation pattern that is very similar to that for the horizontally installed straight version of the antenna on the 160m, 80m and 60m bands and a similar performance can be expected. However, there is a slight increase in the RF energy radiated skywards and this tends to increase for the bands above 60m.

For the double-L configuration, generally up to 15% of the length of each leg can be bent over without significantly changing the radiation pattern of the antenna on the lower and mid HF bands. However, any changes to the antenna's legs should be symmetrical to maintain the balance of the antenna.

### 6.1.6 Loading a G5RV Antenna

It is possible to operate a G5RV antenna on a lower band by adding a loading coil into each leg of the antenna's wire span with a short length of wire extending beyond each loading coil. The concept of this antenna is shown in Figure 6.3(a).

The loading coils retune the wire span and the antenna is brought to resonance on the lower band by adjusting the length of the wire extending beyond each loading coil. This technique enables, for example, a G5RV antenna devised to operate on the 80m band to be used on 160m band. The overall length of the antenna's wire span is lengthened to enable the antenna to be retuned, however the length of the modified antenna is still less than a G5RV antenna constructed for use the 160m band. The length of wire extending beyond each loading coil has a capacitive reactance and this is used, in conjunction with the loading coils' reactance, to bring the antenna to resonance on the lower band.

Example using the 80m version of the G5RV antenna: This version of the G5RV antenna had a wire span of 31.1m long. The space available allowed the wire span to be extended by at least 6.25m at each end, giving a theoretic length of 44.1m. Although 44.1m may seem long, this length

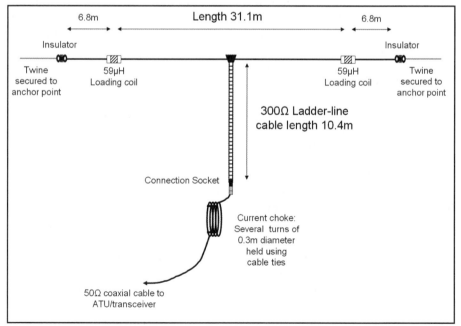

**Figure 6.3(a): details of how the 80m version of the G5RV antenna can be modified using loading coils to enable operation on the 160m band.**

is around 19m shorter than the wire span required for the 160m version (ie 63.2m).

Using the information from Section 3.1.1, 6.25m of wire is equivalent to a capacitor of about 31.25pF. There are two lengths of wire used to extend the antenna, giving

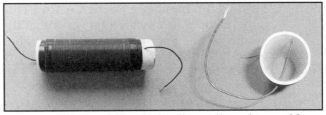

**Figure 6.3(b): Example of a loading coil used to enable an 80m G5RV to be tuned for use on the 160m band.**

an overall capacitance of 62.5pF. This capacitance (C) is required to resonate the loading coils (L) on the 160m. Taking 1.85MHz for this frequency (f), it is possible to calculate the inductance required is given by:

$$L(\mu H) = \frac{1}{4 \times \pi^2 \times f^2 \times C}$$

$$= \frac{1}{4 \times \pi^2 \times (1.85 \times 10^6)^2 \times (62.5 \times 10^{-12})}$$

$$= 118 \mu H$$

This inductance is equally divided between each leg of the wire span as two 59μH loading coils. The approximate number of turns required to wind an inductor is given by equation (14) [10] (see Section 3.9.1):

$$\text{Number of turns} \approx \frac{\sqrt{(457.2) \times (L) \times (D) + (1016 \times \text{Len} \times L)}}{D} \qquad [14]$$

Taking a loading coil of length 120mm (Len), diameter 40mm (D), then the turns required for a loading coil of 59μH is given by:

$$\frac{\left((457.2 \times 59 \times 40) + (1016 \times 120 \times 59)\right)^{\frac{1}{2}}}{40} \approx \textbf{72 turns}$$

Two loading coils were made up of 72 turns wound using 0.7mm diameter stranded copper wire onto a PVC tube of diameter 40mm. These were connected to the ends of an 80m version of the G5RV antenna. 6.25m of the same wire was then connected to the end of each loading coil. Initially the antenna was found to resonate at around 2.0MHz and the extension wires were lengthened to 6.8m, allowing the antenna to resonate on 1.9MHz. This allowed the antenna to be used on the 160m with an ATU to enable the performance of the antenna to be maximised. The loading coils act as chokes on higher frequencies, enabling operation on the 80m and 60m bands (and above), although the use of an ATU is recommended to obtain the best performance.

The predicted horizontal and vertical radiation patterns for this loaded version of the G5RV were found to be very similar to those predicted for the 160m version of the G5RV for the 160m and 80m bands (Figure 6.2). However, for this loaded antenna, the predicted horizontal and vertical radiation patterns for the 60m band are very similar to those predicted for the 80m band (see Section 6.1.4). This is to be expected because the antenna operates as an 80m version of the G5RV due to the loading coils acting as chokes on this band (and above). Another advantage of this antenna is that the ladder-line used for the feeder cable did not need to be extended, however an ATU is needed to enable the performance of the antenna to be maximised.

The loaded version of the G5RV antenna was used for several years enabling many contacts to be made across Europe and into North America on the 160m band. The antenna's details have been included in Figure 6.3(a) and an example of one of the loading coils used is shown in Figure 6.3(b).

## 6.2 Doublet Antennas

The doublet comprises a wire span fed at its centre with balanced two-wire feeder cable. The length of the wire span should be an electrical half wavelength ($\lambda/2$) long at the lowest frequency of operation and gives a length of around 77m when operating at 1.85MHz. However, the wire span can be reduced to three-eights of an electrical wavelength ($3\lambda/8$) in length without significantly compromising the performance of the antenna [19]. The balanced two-wire feeder can be open-wire or ladder-line cable and has the advantage that it is low loss. If ladder-line is used, this can be either to the 300$\Omega$ or 450$\Omega$ varieties. The length of the balanced two-wire feeder cable can be cut to suit the requirements where the antenna is to be installed.

This is a balanced antenna and it is brought to resonance using an ATU that has a balanced input. The end of the balanced feeder cable can present a wide variation of impedance and the ATU used needs to be capable handling this wide range. Figure 6.4 illustrates the concept of the doublet antenna and this arrangement is often referred to as the tuned doublet or random-length dipole.

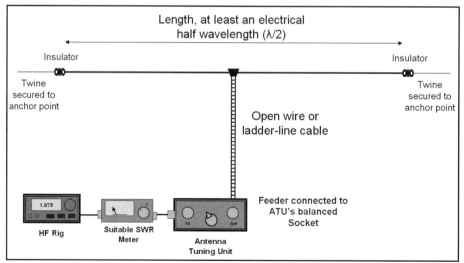

**Figure 6.4: Concept of the doublet antenna. This arrangement is often referred to as the tuned doublet or random-length dipole.**

When balanced feeder cable is passed over a metal window frame, guttering, flashing, domestic wiring, or similar conductive surface, this can cause the currents flowing in the feeder cable to become unbalanced. This unbalance of the currents can degrade the performance of the antenna through common mode problems. This problem can be avoided by running a coaxial cable from the ATU's 50Ω unbalanced connection to the antenna using a balun to interface the unbalanced coaxial cable to the balanced feeder. The self-screening properties of coaxial cable allow it to be run in close proximity to metal surfaces without common mode problems being incurred. However, the length of the coaxial cable used should be as short as possible to keep the losses to a minimum (coax gets very lossy when it is used away from its design impedance). The impedance presented at the balanced feeder cable's end depends upon the length of the feeder cable. Therefore, the balun used may need to be a 4:1 impedance ratio type, rather than a 1:1 impedance ratio type. The construction of baluns is described within Chapter 8. This version of the doublet antenna is sometimes referred to as a Coaxial Cable Fed Multi-band Dipole (Comudipole) [20]. Figure 6.5 illustrates the concept of the doublet antenna fed using this using arrangement.

### 6.2.1 Doublet with Minimised SWR

The technique described is based on the design by Cecil Moore, W6RCA, devised for a doublet antenna that did not need an ATU [20]. This antenna design is based on a conventional centrally fed wire span with a balanced ladder-line feeder run down to the radio equipment. The design could be used with either 300Ω or 450Ω ladder-line cable types. The physical length of the ladder-line feeder is changed to suit the band in use so that

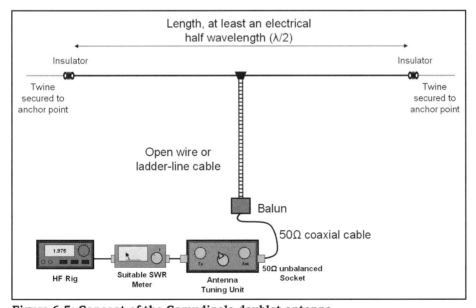

**Figure 6.5: Concept of the Comudipole doublet antenna.**

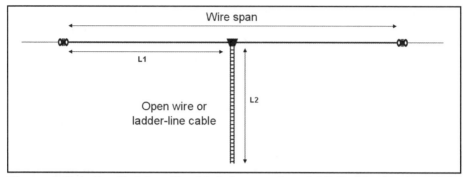

**Figure 6.6(a): Doublet lengths L1 (wire span) and L2 (ladder-line) used in W6RCA's calculations.**

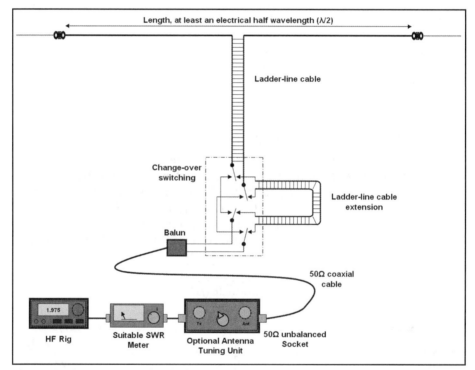

**Figure 6.6(b): Concept of a doublet based on W6RCA's ladder-line switching system. This uses a DPDT (changeover) relay to extend the ladder-line to use the antenna on 160m and 60m from 80m.**

a current maximum always coincides at the bottom of the ladder-line. The ladder-line's input impedance at this point will be low and non-reactive giving a low SWR. This allows the direct connection of the transceiver to the ladder-line feeder, using a length of coaxial cable and a 1:1 choke balun to minimise any imbalance between the twin-line feeder and the radio equipment. However, good practice is still use an ATU to obtain the best performance.

The concept of the antenna is shown in Figure 6.6(a) where the length of each doublet leg is L1 and the ladder-line feeder is L2 (allowing for the ladder-line's velocity factor (v)). A reasonable match can be obtained when the total length of L1 plus L2 is an odd multiple of an electrical quarter wavelength ($\lambda/4$) on the band in use where the length can be estimated from:

$$L1 + \left(L2 \times v\right) = n \times \frac{\lambda}{4} \qquad [22]$$

where v is the velocity factor and n is 3, 5, 7, 9 and so on.

Rearranging equation (22) to estimate the length of the ladder line L2 for a 160m band doublet, centred on 1.85MHz, where L1 is 40.55 long ($\lambda/4$ in free space), n is equal to 3 and the velocity factor is 0.95 gives:

$$\text{Ladder-line length L2 (m)} \approx \frac{(3 \times 40.55) - 40.55m}{(.95)} \approx 85.37m$$

Using 40.55m for L1 gives a combined length of the ladder-line and a quarter wavelength length of the wire span (L1 + L2.v) is approximates to 126m (125.92m). The length of the doublet's wire span is twice 40.55m, or 81.1m in length. This is slightly longer than an electrical half-wavelength and provides an allowance enabling the wire span to be trimmed when tuning the antenna should this be necessary.

When operating on the 80m band, centred on 3.65MHz, this wire span length is close to a wavelength. The antenna's combined length of 126m can accommodate close to 6 quarter-waves on the 80m band (ie $\lambda/4$ is 20.55m at 3.65MHz). Therefore, the antenna can be expected to present a poor match on 80m because operation will be close to a voltage maximum. However, 5 quarter-waves on the 80m band can be accommodated if the ladder-line is reduced to around 62.2m in length (ie with the antenna's combined length shorted to around 103m). This could be achieved by disconnecting 23.2m of ladder-line cable to shorten it to 62.2m by using a suitable switching arrangement.

When operating on the 60m band, centred on a frequency centred of 5.32MHz, the 81.1m long wire span length is close to a three half wavelengths. The antenna's combined length of 126m is very close to 9 quarter-waves on the 60m band (ie $\lambda/4$ is 14.1m at 5.32MHz). Therefore, the 126m long balanced feeder's end presents a low impedance and consequently a low SWR enabling operation on the 60m band.

Figure 6.6(b) shows a doublet antenna based on W6RCA's concept, where a ladder-line extension is switched in to make the line 126m long. This allows the antenna to be used on the 160m and 60m bands with a low SWR presented at the ladder-line cable's end. Switching the ladder-line extension out shortens the line to 62.2m enabling operation on 80m with a low SWR presented at the end of the ladder-line cable. The switching system used two relays with change-over contacts (or DPDT, Double Pole Double Throw) to switch the ladder-line extension in or out, with the relays controlled remotely from the shack. The switching system could be housed in a weatherproof box with a control cable run to the shack.

The length of the ladder-line cable in this arrangement is long and it is possible to coil the up a section the ladder-line into large loops forming a helical cylinder of about 1m diameter to allow it to be accommodated within the space available. W6RCA devised a rack to hold several loops of ladder-line that had a separation of several centimetres between the loops to minimise induction between them.

This adjustable antenna system offers a solution to operate on the 160m, 80m and 60m bands using an auto-ATU where the range of SWR that can be handled can be limited (eg often up to around 3:1). The arrangement also has the advantage that a manual ATU does not have to be capable of continually handling higher RF voltages associated with a high SWR.

### 6.2.2 Predicted Radiation Patterns

Figure 6.7 shows the predicted radiation patterns in the horizontal and vertical planes for a doublet antenna using the MMANA-GAL antenna analysis application [7] whose wire span is 79m long and installed at 20m agl. The radiation patterns are representative of those expected for the tuned doublet, Comudipole and W6RCA derivative antennas previously described.

On the 160m and 80m bands, the horizontal radiation patterns are very similar and indicate close to omnidirectional radiation, with the performance on 80m having a slight improvement compared to that on 160m. However, on the 60m band, the horizontal radiation pattern has significant nulls and there are lobes extending off the ends and broadside to the wire span. This is because the wire span is close to 1.5 wavelengths long when used on 60m, resulting in the formation of a multi-lobed radiation pattern.

The vertical radiation pattern for 160m and 80m are very similar with much of the radiation directed skywards. This makes the antenna suited to more localised skip allowing contacts to be made up to around 800km on the 160m and 80m bands. However, depending upon the propagation

**Figure 6.7:**
**MMANA-GAL predict-
ed radiation patterns
for the W6RCA based
doublet on 160m,
80m and 60m with
the wire span at 20m
agl.**

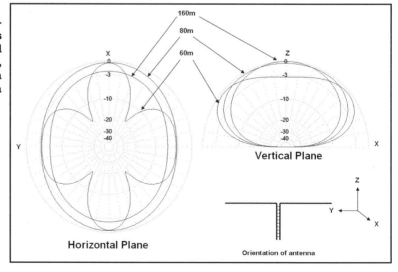

conditions the antenna does enable more distant stations to be worked on 160m and 80m because some radiation is directed at a lower angle towards the horizon. On the 60m band, the vertical radiation pattern tends to be directed at a lower angle towards the horizon compared to 160m and 80m. This enables more distant stations to be worked provided the propagation conditions are suitable on the 60m band.

## 6.3 The Off Centre Fed Dipole

The Off Centre Fed Dipole (OCFD) is a multi-band antenna whose wire span is an electrical half wavelength long at its lowest frequency of operation (f MHz). However, the OCFD's feed point is located one third of the way along the wire span from one end [21]. At this point, the feed point's impedance is around 150 to 200Ω at the lowest frequency of operation, although the height of the antenna above the ground and the proximity of any close objects will also have an effect on the antenna's impedance [22].

When the OFCD is fed with a signal that is the second harmonic of the lowest operational frequency (ie 2f MHz), the impedance at the feed point continues to be around 100 to 200Ω. Similarly, if the applied signal is the fourth (4f MHz) or the eighth harmonic (8f MHz), then the feed point's impedance continues to be around 100 to 200Ω.

An explanation why the antenna performs in this way is illustrated in Figure 6.8 for frequencies of f, 2f and 4f MHz for a half-wavelength antenna using the current SWR distribution along the wire span. A similar series of curves for the voltage SWR will also exist along the wire span at f, 2f and 4f MHz that are phase shifted by 90°. However, to keep the explanation to follow straightforward, only the current SWR distribution has been used.

The curve representing the SWR at f MHz is typical of the current SWR distribution for a half-wavelength wire span (see Figure 2.1). Superimposed on the diagram are the current SWR distributions 2f MHz and 4f MHz. At a third of the length along the wire span the curves all cross (ie at 60°) and there is a similar point when the length becomes two thirds (ie at 120°). This implies that the impedance at these points is the same at all three frequencies as indicated by the vertical broken lines. Therefore, a feeder cable could be connected to a feed point located at one third of the length

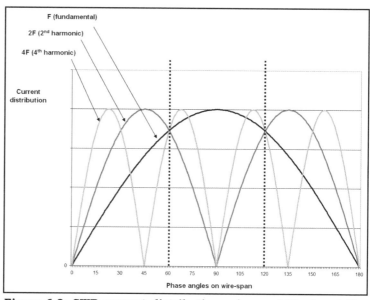

**Figure 6.8: SWR current distributions along a λ/2 wire at the resonant frequency f, 2nd harmonic 2f and 4th harmonic 4f.**

from the wire span's end enabling the antenna to be operated at these frequencies with a reasonably low SWR.

If a 300Ω ladder-line twin cable is connected to the antenna's feed point and terminated with a 4:1 matching transformer, then the SWR seen at the transformer's input can be expected to be around 2:1 to 3:1 at frequencies f, 2f and 4f MHz referred to 50Ω (and 8f, 16f and so on). This allows the antenna to be within the tuning range of most commercial ATUs and auto-ATUs. The concept of an OFCD fed using 300Ω ladder-line is illustrated in Figure 6.9.

The OCFD antenna is inherently unbalanced because the feeder cable is not placed symmetrically with respect to the antenna's radiated field. Secondly, the antenna's legs, being of different lengths, present slightly unequal impedances. The effect of these is to cause common mode currents to flow on the feeder line. However, this is not always a disadvantage because radiation from the feeder cable can help to improve the radiation pattern by reducing any null points present [23].

An OCFD antenna for use on the 160m and 80m bands has a wire span length of 84m that is fed using a balanced 2-wire feeder cable connected 28m from one end. These dimensions have been included within Figure 6.9 for reference. The OCFD antenna can also be used for operation on the 60m band. The operation of the antenna on the 60m band can be considered as an offset fed doublet and the length of the feeder cable affects the impedance that it presents at its end. This necessitates the use of an ATU to tune the antenna to maximise its performance.

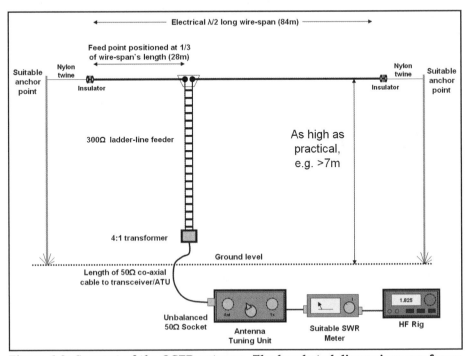

**Figure 6.9: Concept of the OCFD antenna. The bracketed dimensions are for an OCFD devised for 160m and 80m, and 60m using an ATU.**

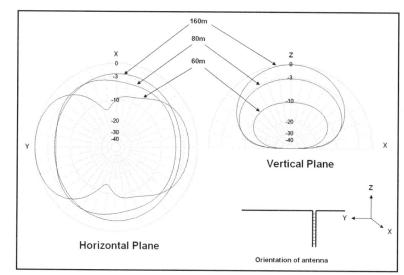

**Figure 6.10:**
MMANA-GAL predicted radiation patterns for the OCFD antenna on 160m, 80m and 60m with the wire span at 16m agl fed with 15m of balanced 2-wire feeder cable.

### 6.3.1 Predicted Radiation Pattern

To obtain an indication of the performance of an OCFD antenna covering the 160m, 80m and 60m bands, a MMANA-GAL [7] antenna model was constructed. This model comprised an 84m long wire-span, fed one third of its length using a 15m long balanced feeder cable. The model was run with the antenna at 16m above the ground.

Figure 6.10 illustrates the predicted horizontal and vertical radiation patterns obtained from the model using 1.85MHz, 3.65MHz and 5.32MHz as representative frequencies of operation:

***160m band:***
- the horizontal pattern is close to omni-directional and indicates reasonable coverage in all directions
- the vertical pattern indicates most of the radiation goes ·skyward above an angle of 40° indicating a more localised 'skip' radius (typically allowing contacts to be made up to around an 800km radius). However, occasionally DX contacts are possible because some lower angle radiation occurs from 15° to 30°.

***80m band:***
- the horizontal pattern is similar to that for 160m, although it is not as uniform. However, the radiation pattern indicates reasonable coverage in all directions.
- the vertical pattern is similar to that for 160m with most of the radiation directed skywards. However, the radiation pattern shows a slightly lower intensity compared to that for 160m. Most of the radiation goes skyward above an angle of 40° indicating a more localised "skip" radius (typically allowing contacts to be made up to around an 800km radius). However, occasionally DX contacts are possible because some lower angle radiation occurs from 15° to 30°.

### 60m band:

- the horizontal pattern shows a null developing either side of the wire span and there is evidence of some directivity off the ends of the antenna. The prediction shows significant radiation directed either side of the wire span, although stations received broadside on to the wire span could be around 1 to 2 S-Points down compared to those received off the ends of the antenna.
- the vertical pattern predicts that the radiation tends to be at low angle radiation towards the horizon. This indicates the antenna should have an acceptable performance for DX contacts on 60m, with potentially longer distance stations being worked off the ends of the antenna.
- it should be noted that the radiation patterns predicted with the antenna at 16m agl when operating on the 60m band. The radiation patterns predicted will tend to differ if the antenna is significantly higher or lower than 16m agl. Consequently, the radiation patterns illustrated only provide an indication of the operation of the antenna at 60m.

### 6.4 Doublet, G5RV and OCFD Antenna Construction and Installation

Details covering the construction and installation of doublet type antennas are very similar to those described in Section 5.4 for the dipole antenna. To follow are examples and techniques that apply to the doublet type of antenna.

The arrangement used to connect the balanced twin-line cable to each leg of the doublet antenna is often suspended within the antenna's span and necessitates a physically strong but lightweight design. Commercially, there are various designs available and a typical dog-bone type dipole centre that was acquired at a radio rally (as illustrated previously in Figure 5.8). This type of dipole centre can be obtained from various suppliers and there are several variations available.

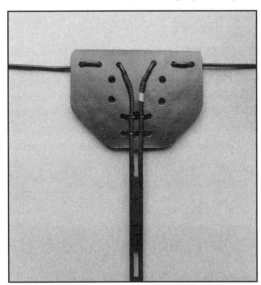

A doublet centre made from a sheet of 3mm thick uPVC (unplasticized polyvinyl chloride) is shown in Figure 6.11 where the feeder cable used is 300Ω ladder-line. This design had three holes drilled along the upper section of the dipole centre either side of the middle as shown. Each wire leg of the doublet was then held in place by lacing it through the holes as shown. Two rows of three holes were then drilled into the lower section of the dipole centre to hold the balanced twin-line feeder cable (eg ladder-line) in place using cable ties passed through the holes, laced around the bal-

**Figure 6.11: The dipole centre used in for a doublet antenna fed with 300Ω ladder-line. The lighter coloured sleeving helps to identify the ladder line connections at each end of the cable.**

anced twin-line feeder cable and tightened as shown. Two larger diameter holes were drilled symmetrically either side above where the feeder cable was attached to allow the antenna to be installed as an inverted-V if necessary. A short length of heatshrink is passed over each doublet leg and the leg soldered to one of the feeder cable's conductors. After soldering, the joint was protected by wrapping several layers of plumbers' PTFE tape around it. Then the heatshrink was slid over each joint and shrunk using a heat-gun to help weatherproof the joint. The choice of uPVC for the dipole centre was made because this material is designed for use outside in the wet, is fairly rugged and is able to generally withstand degradation from sunlight.

The doublet can be supported using 2mm or 3mm diameter nylon twine with 'dog bone' insulators at the ends of the dipole's legs. When measuring up the wire for each doublet leg, an extra length of about 150mm should be added at each end to give an allowance for connecting the dipole leg to the centre insulator and the end insulator. If each wire end is threaded through the insulator to form a loop, then this allows the length of each dipole leg to be adjusted for minimum SWR by folding the wire back on itself. However, it is important that the antenna is kept symmetrical during this procedure. Once the optimum lengths have been found, cable ties can be used to secure each wire end in place. It is recommended not to use egg insulators and wire as the wire span's leg end supports because this can increase the end capacitance causing the antenna's performance to be unpredictable.

The doublet and G5RV antenna's geometry can be altered by converting it into an inverted-V or by bending the ends down to enable the antenna to be fitted into a smaller space without modification to the length. Generally, up to 15% of the length of each leg can be bent over without significantly changing the radiation pattern of the antenna on the lower and mid HF bands. However, any changes to the antenna's legs should be symmetrical to maintain the balance of the antenna. When installing an OCFD antenna it is important to install the antenna as a straight wire run horizontally with respect to the ground to obtain the best performance.

## 6.5 MF Magnetic Loop Antenna Practicalities

A magnetic loop antenna might seem a suitable solution where the length of a MF wire antenna is undesirably long or conspicuous. But magnetic loop antennas for 630m or 160m would be quite big and heavy. One covering the 80m to 60m bands may be practical, depending upon the space available.

A magnetic loop antenna consists of a conductive loop, a suitable series tuning capacitor and an arrangement to couple the antenna to the transceiver, usually a Faraday loop of coax of about one-eighth of the main loop diameter. See Figure 6.12. It is brought to resonance using the tuning capacitor, and can give an operating range of 1:2 (eg 1.85 to 3.7MHz). The loop's circumference should be from $0.125\lambda$ to $0.25\lambda$. If it is longer than $0.25\lambda$ it tends to behave as an electric field rather than a magnetic field antenna.

Radiation resistance is a function of the area enclosed by the loop and

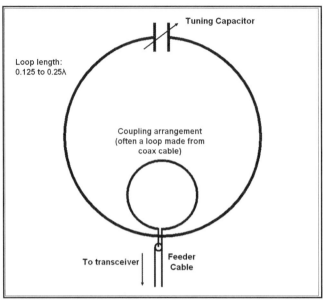

Loop length:
0.125 to 0.25λ

Tuning Capacitor

Coupling arrangement
(often a loop made from
coax cable)

To transceiver

Feeder
Cable

**Figure 6.12: Concept of a magnetic loop antenna and its coupling arrangement.**

is highest for a circular loop. For good radiation efficiency it is important to minimise the ratio between RF ohmic losses and the radiation resistance. The losses comprise the resistance of the loop and the tuning capacitor (which tends to be the lower of the two). Skin effect causes the RF current to flow only on the outer surface of the loop, so a large diameter conductor (eg >25mm) should be used to maximise surface area. Magnetic loop antennas for use on and below 160m have a long loop conductor and consequently higher RF ohmic losses than smaller, higher frequency antennas.

| Frequency | Wavelength | 0.25λ Loop | |
|---|---|---|---|
| | | Length | Diameter |
| 474kHz | 633m | 158m | 50.3m |
| 1.85MHz | 162m | 40.5m | 13m |
| 3.65MHz | 82m | 20.5m | 6.5m |
| 5.32MHz | 56m | 14m | 4.5m |

**Table 6.1: Suggested MF magnetic loop dimensions.**

The magnetic loop antenna has a high Q-factor. This results in a narrow effective bandwidth and requires retuning for quite small changes in frequency. The RF voltage across the tuning capacitor – and the current through it – are both high, around 1500V and 2.5A for a 160m magnetic loop driven at 10W. One must use a good quality transmitting-type capacitor, typically a wide-spaced split-stator type of about 240pF per section, with each section connected in series to eliminate rotor contact losses.

The high-Q properties of a magnetic loop also dramatically reduce any harmonic radiation. In utilising the near-field magnetic component of the electromagnetic wave, it has a further advantage over an electric field antenna in that nearby objects absorb much less RF energy.

Table 6.1 suggests dimensions for a single-turn magnetic loop antenna for various bands. A 0.25λ magnetic loop may be practical for 80m if there is sufficient room. Using a suitable capacitor this loop could also be tuned for 160m, at reduced efficiency. Similarly, a 60m antenna could be tuned for 80m.

**7**

# Directional Antennas

Directional antennas for use on the 160m, 80m and 60m bands tend to be large and consequently require a significant area of ground for their installation. From a practical perspective, large beam antennas tend not to be able to be rotated and are set up to beam a signal in a particular direction. If access to a significant area of ground is available, then a fixed large HF beam antenna could be a possibility for use on 160m, 80m and 60m. However, a beam antenna for the 630m band tends not to be a practical possibility due to it physical size.

The antennas previously described had each of their horizontal and vertical radiation patterns presented on a single diagram for ease of comparison. However, for the V-beam and rhombic antennas, their radiation patterns are not straightforward to interpret when plotted on a single diagram. Therefore, the radiation patterns for the V-beam and rhombic antennas have been illustrated separately for ease of viewing in the descriptions to follow. The radiation patterns have been shown orientated in the X axis rather than the Y axis as used in the previous diagrams. This was to allow the antenna's directivity in the vertical radiation plane to be shown.

The *Radio Communication Handbook* [24] provides guidance covering the design and operation of beam antennas for these bands and the following is provided as an overview.

### 7.1 V-beams

There are two forms of V-beam:

- the bi-directional V-beam
- the unidirectional V-beam.

Each is described separately in the following sections.

### 7.1.1 Bi-directional V-Beam

The V-beam consists of two wires made in the form of a V and fed at the apex with a balanced twin-wire feeder, as shown in Figure 7.1. A long-wire antenna, two wavelengths long and fed at the end has four lobes of maximum radiation at an angle of 36° to the wire. If two such antennas are erected horizontally to form a V, that has an included angle of 72°, then some lobes will tend to be in alignment and are additive in the direction of the bisector of the apex. The other lobes will tend to be out of alignment and cancel. The result is a pronounced bi-directional beam. The directivity and gain of V-beams depends on the length of the legs and the angle at the apex of the V. This is likely to be the limiting factor in most amateur installations and is the first point to be considered when designing a V-beam. The gain in the most favourable direction to be expected for a given apex angle are given in Table 7.1.

| Leg length (Wavelength) | Gain (dBd) | Apex Angle (Degrees) |
|---|---|---|
| 1 | 3 | 108 |
| 2 | 4.5 | 70 |
| 3 | 5.5 | 57 |
| 4 | 6.5 | 47 |

Table 7.1: V-beam gain and apex angles for given lengths of element.

### 7.1.1.1 Predicted Radiation Patterns

A MMANA-GAL [7] predicted horizontal and vertical plane radiation pattern for a V-beam is shown in Figure 7.2. The antenna modelled had legs each of 164.4m long corresponding to two wavelengths at 3.65MHz on the 80m band. The antenna was modelled at 20m agl and was installed horizontally above the ground. The predicted horizontal and vertical radiation patterns shown are for antenna operated at representative frequencies of 1.85MHz, 3.65MHz and 5.32MHz.

Figure 7.2(a) shows the predicted radiation patterns for the antenna modelled on the 160m band. The horizontal radiation pattern indicates that some bi-directional radiation is evident. However, the antenna's directivity is not significant because each leg of the antenna is close to a wavelength long. The verti-

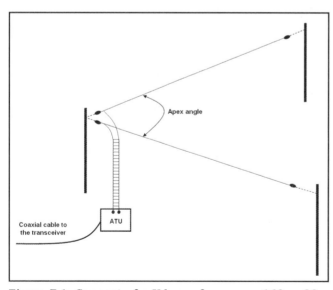

Figure 7.1: Concept of a V-beam for use on 160m, 80m and 60m where each leg comprising the V is at least a wavelength long at the lower operating frequency. A balanced line ATU should be used to ensure an equal current level in each leg.

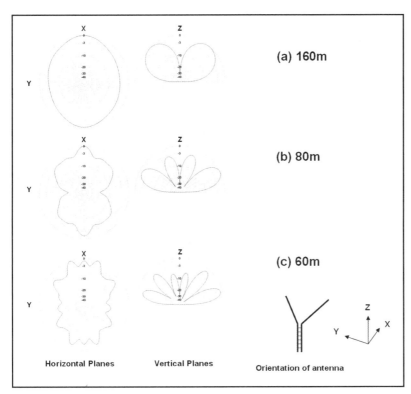

Figure 7.2:
MMANA-GAL predicted radiation patterns for the V-beam on 160m, 80m and 60m showing the antenna's bi-directional radiation pattern.

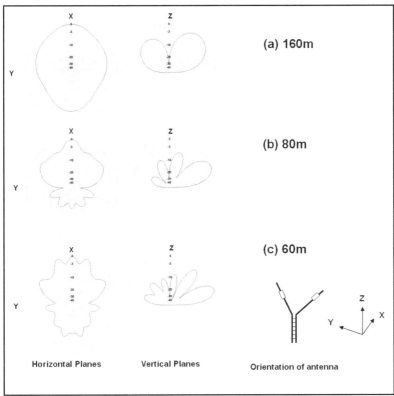

Figure 7.3:
MMANA-GAL predicted radiation patterns for the V-beam on 160m, 80m and 60m showing the antenna's unidirectional radiation pattern when each leg includes a 500Ω resistor connected λ/4 from the end.

cal radiation pattern shows two lobes of near equal magnitudes radiated forwards of and behind the antenna.

Figure 7.2(b) shows the predicted radiation patterns for the antenna on the 80m band, where each leg of the antenna has become close to two wavelengths long. The horizontal radiation pattern indicates that the antenna has become more bi-directional and nulls have formed either side of the orientation of the antenna. The vertical radiation pattern shows four lobes have formed, with two radiated forward and two radiated behind the antenna either side of the Z axis, the lobes are nearly symmetrical indicating the bi-directional characteristic of this antenna.

Figure 7.2(c) shows the predicted radiation patterns on the 60m band. Each leg of the antenna is now approximately three wavelengths long and the antenna starts to show directivity. The horizontal radiation pattern indicates that more radiation is directed ahead of the antenna than behind it. The vertical radiation pattern shows six lobes have formed, with the three radiated forward being slightly larger in magnitude compared to the rear three lobes radiated behind the antenna. The vertical radiation pattern also demonstrates that the antenna becomes more directional as the frequency of operation is increased.

For all three radiation patterns shown, the MMANA-GAL [7] model predicted a front to back ratio for the antenna of around 0.3 to 1dB, indicating that the antenna is primarily a bi-directional radiator but tending to radiate slightly more RF energy ahead of it as the frequency is increased.

### 7.1.2 The Unidirectional V-Beam

The V-beam can be made unidirectional if it is terminated with resistors inserted approximately a quarter wavelength from the ends of the legs so that final quarter-wavelengths act as artificial earths. A suitable value of resistor is 500Ω for each leg. Termination resistors have the effect of absorbing some of the lobes produced and the legs become travelling wave devices.

### 7.1.2.1 Predicted Radiation Patterns

A MMANA-GAL [7] predicted horizontal and vertical plane radiation pattern for a V-beam is shown in Figure 7.3. The antenna modelled had legs each of 164.4m long corresponding to two wavelengths at 3.65MHz on the 80m band. In a similar way to the previous V-beam, the included angle between the antenna's legs was 72°. Each leg included a 500Ω resistor connected 20.55m from its end (ie λ/4 at 3.65MHz). The antenna was modelled at 20m agl and was installed horizontally above the ground. The predicted horizontal and vertical radiation patterns shown are for antenna operated at representative frequencies of 1.85MHz, 3.65MHz and 5.32MHz.

Figure 7.3(a) shows the predicted radiation patterns for antenna modelled on the 160m band. The horizontal radiation pattern indicates that more radiation is directed ahead of the antenna than behind it showing that the antenna has started to develop gain, although the model predicted a gain of only about 1dBi. The vertical radiation pattern shows the lobe formed ahead of the antenna is larger in magnitude than the lobe behind the antenna. Both the horizontal and vertical radiation patterns indicate that the antenna has become unidirectional as a result of the connection of a 500Ω resistor approximately a quarter wavelength from each wire end.

Figure 7.3(b) shows the predicted radiation patterns on the 80m band where each leg of the antenna has become close to two wavelengths long. The horizontal radiation pattern indicates that the antenna is directional with significant RF radiation ahead of the antenna compared to behind it. The vertical radiation pattern shows four lobes have formed, with two radiated forward and two radiated behind the antenna. The two lobes forward of the antenna have a much greater magnitude compared to the rear lobes indicating gain, with the model predicting around 4dBi. Both the horizontal and vertical radiation patterns further indicate that the antenna has become directional as a result of the connection of a 500Ω resistor approximately a quarter wavelength from each wire end.

Figure 7.3(c) shows the predicted radiation patterns on the 60m band. Each leg of the antenna is now approximately three wavelengths long and the antenna's directivity is evident. The horizontal radiation pattern indicates that more radiation is directed ahead of the antenna than behind it, with a gain of about 5.3dBi predicted. The vertical radiation pattern shows six lobes have formed, with the three radiated forward being larger in magnitude compared to the rear three lobes radiated behind the antenna. The vertical radiation pattern also demonstrates that the antenna has become even more directional as the frequency of operation is increased.

### 7.1.3 V-Beam Installation

V-beams are often constructed so that the apex is placed as high as possible with the ends close to the ground. This arrangement means that only one mast is required for the installation and, if space is available, several V-beams pointing in different directions could use a common support. The input impedance of this antenna may rise to 2000Ω in a short V, but will be between 800 and 1000Ω in a longer antenna. Therefore, 400 to 600Ω feed lines can be used that are matched to the transceiver with a suitable balanced ATU.

### 7.2 The Rhombic

The rhombic antenna is a V-beam with a second V added as illustrated in Figure 7.4. In a similar manner as the V-beam, the rhombic antenna uses the same lobe addition

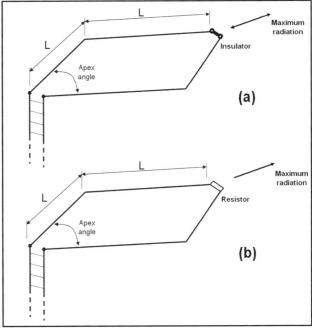

**Figure 7.4: The Rhombic antenna. Drawing (a) shows the un-terminated version and (b) the terminated version.**

**Figure 7.5:** MMANA-GAL predicted radiation patterns for the rhombic antenna on 160m, 80m and 60m showing the antenna's bi-directional radiation pattern when the antenna's end is open circuit.

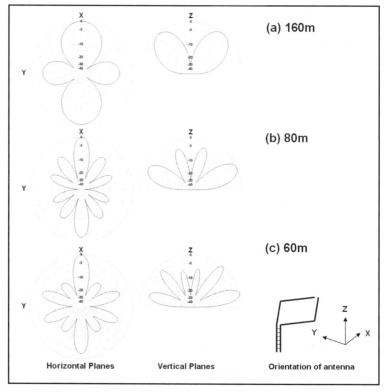

**Figure 7.6:** MMANA-GAL predicted radiation patterns for the terminated rhombic antenna on 160m, 80m and 60m showing the antenna's unidirectional radiation pattern when the antenna's end is terminated with resistive load.

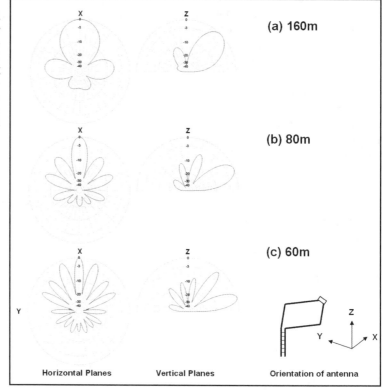

principle. However, there is an additional factor to be considered because the lobes from the front and rear halves must also add in phase at the required elevation angle. This introduces an extra degree of control in the design so that considerable variation of pattern can be obtained by choosing various apex angles and heights above ground. The rhombic gives an increased gain compared to the V-beam, however its size necessitates more space to accommodate it and requires at least one extra support compared to the V-beam.

There are two forms of the rhombic antenna:

- bi-directional rhombic
- unidirectional rhombic.

Each is described separately within the following sections.

## 7.2.1 The Bi-directional Rhombic

When a rhombic antenna is terminated by an open-circuit at its far end, the antenna's radiation pattern is bi-directional and is similar to that for the bi-directional V-beam described previously. The concept of this type of rhombic antenna is shown in Figure 7.4(a).

### 7.2.1.1 Predicted Radiation Patterns

A MMANA-GAL [7] predicted horizontal and vertical plane radiation pattern for a bi-directional rhombic antenna is shown in Figure 7.5. The antenna modelled had four legs each of 164.4m in length connected in a rhombic shape to form the antenna as shown, with each leg corresponding to two wavelengths at 3.65MHz on the 80m band (ie a wire length of close to four wavelengths on the 80m band). In a similar way to the previous V-beam, the included angle between the antenna's legs was 72°. The antenna was modelled at 20m agl and was installed horizontally above the ground. The predicted horizontal and vertical radiation patterns shown are for antenna operated at representative frequencies of 1.85MHz, 3.65MHz and 5.32MHz.

Figure 7.5(a) shows the predicted radiation patterns for the rhombic antenna modelled on the 160m band, where each wire of the antenna has become close to two wavelengths long. The horizontal radiation pattern indicates that bi-directional radiation is very evident. However, large side lobes have formed either side of the antenna's orientation. The vertical radiation pattern shows two lobes of near equal magnitudes radiated forwards of and behind the antenna.

Figure 7.5(b) shows the predicted radiation patterns for the antenna on the 80m band, where each wire of the antenna has become close to four wavelengths long. The horizontal radiation pattern indicates that the antenna has become more directional and four side lobes have developed either side of the antenna's orientation. The vertical radiation pattern shows four lobes have formed, with two radiated forward and two radiated behind the antenna either side of the Z axis, the lobes are not quite symmetrical, indicating that the antenna has become slightly more directional.

Figure 7.5(c) shows the predicted radiation patterns on the 60m band, where each wire of the antenna is now approximately six wavelengths long.

The horizontal radiation pattern is very similar to that on 80m with four side lobes either side of the antenna's orientation. However, the two side lobes each side of the antenna's X-axis, that are directed at about 20° to the Y-axis, are of a greater magnitude compared to the two other lobes directed at about 50°. The vertical radiation pattern shows six lobes have formed and is similar to that for 80m. The three lobes radiated forward are slightly larger in magnitude compared to the rear three lobes radiated behind the antenna. The vertical radiation pattern also demonstrates that the antenna becomes more directional as the frequency of operation is increased.

For all three radiation patterns shown, the MMANA-GAL [7] model predicted a front to back ratio for the antenna of around 1 to 2dB, indicating that the antenna is primarily a bi-directional radiator but tending to radiate slightly more RF energy ahead if it as the frequency is increased. The equivalent V-beam had a predicted front-to-back ratio around 0.3 to 1dB for comparison.

### 7.2.2 The Terminated Rhombic

The terminated version of the Rhombic, as shown in Figure 7.4(b), has a unidirectional pattern and is a travelling wave antenna. The terminating resistance absorbs noise and interference coming from the rear direction as well as transmitter power, that otherwise would be radiated backwards. This means signal-to-noise ratio is improved by up to 3dB without affecting signals transmitted in the wanted direction.

### 7.2.2.1 Predicted Radiation Patterns

A MMANA-GAL [7] predicted horizontal and vertical plane radiation pattern for a unidirectional rhombic antenna is shown in Figure 7.6. The antenna modelled had legs each of 164.4m long connected in a rhombic shape corresponding to two wavelengths at 3.65MHz on the 80m band (ie a wire length of close to four wavelengths on the 80m band). In a similar way to the previous terminated V-beam, the included angle between the antenna's legs was 72°. The end of the rhombic antenna was terminated in an 800Ω load, turning the antenna into a travelling wave device. The antenna was modelled at 20m agl and was installed horizontally above the ground. The predicted horizontal and vertical radiation patterns shown are for antenna operated at representative frequencies of 1.85MHz, 3.65MHz and 5.32MHz.

Figure 7.6(a) shows the predicted radiation patterns for antenna modelled on the 160m band, where each wire of the antenna has become close to two wavelengths long. The horizontal radiation pattern shows the antenna as directional with a large lobe radiated ahead of the antenna, although this lobe is directed skywards at around 45°. The horizontal radiation pattern also shows a side lobe situated either side of the orientation of the antenna. Consequently, stations that are situated either side of the antenna may be received at reasonable levels enabling contacts to be made with them. The vertical radiation pattern shows a lobe formed ahead of the antenna that significantly larger compared to the much smaller lobe behind the antenna. The rear lobe is also directed skywards at an acute angle that helps improved the front to back ratio for the antenna. Both the horizontal and vertical radiation patterns indicate that the antenna has become unidirectional as a result of the connection of an 800Ω load resistor at the end of the antenna. For this configuration on the 160m band, the model predicted a gain of around 4dBi and a front to back ratio of about 12dB.

Figure 7.6(b) shows the predicted radiation patterns on the 80m band where each wire forming the rhombic antenna has become close to four wavelengths long. The horizontal radiation pattern indicates that the antenna has become more directional with significant RF radiation ahead of the antenna compared to behind it. Several side lobes have developed that are symmetrically situated either side of the orientation of the antenna. Consequently, stations that are situated either side of the antenna may be received at reasonable levels enabling contacts to be made with them. The vertical radiation pattern shows four lobes have formed, with two large lobes radiated forward of the antenna and two smaller lobes radiated behind the antenna. The larger of the forward lobes is inclined to the horizon at an angle of around 25°. This should give this antenna a reasonable performance ahead of the antenna with longer distance stations being able to be contacted provided the propagation conditions allow. On the 80m band, the model predicted a gain of around 9dBi and a front to back ratio of about 18dB.

Figure 7.3(c) shows the predicted radiation patterns on the 60m band. Each wire forming the rhombic antenna is now approximately six wavelengths long and the antenna's directivity is evident. The horizontal radiation pattern indicates that the antenna has become more directional with significant RF radiation ahead of the antenna compared to behind it. However, the main lobe is narrow and there are a series of side loads that have developed symmetrically either side of the orientation of the antenna. Consequently, stations that are situated either side of the antenna may be received at reasonable levels enabling contacts to be made with them. However, there are deep nulls within the pattern, meaning that some stations may not be receivable because their direction corresponds with a null. The horizontal radiation pattern indicates that more radiation is directed ahead of the antenna than behind it. The vertical radiation pattern shows six lobes have formed, with the three radiated forward being larger in magnitude compared to the rear three lobes radiated behind the antenna. The lower larger forward lobe is inclined to the horizon by around 15° and should enable longer distance stations to be contacted provided the propagation conditions allow. The slightly smaller forward lobe is inclined to the horizon by around 50° and should allow more localised stations to be contacted by means of 'shorter skip' provided the propagation conditions allow. On the 60m band, the model predicted a gain of around 8dBi and a front to back ratio of about 10dB (ie a slightly lower performance compared to 80m).

### 7.2.3 Rhombic Antenna Installation Overview

The use of tuned feeders enables the Rhombic, like the V-beam, to be used on several amateur bands. The terminated Rhombic differs from the

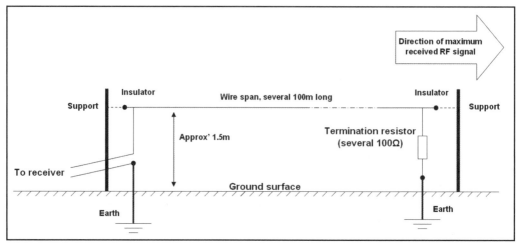

**Figure 7.7: Concept of the Beverage antenna used for *receiving* MF and HF signals.**

open-circuit type (resonant type) by having a non-inductive resistor connected at the far end. This resistor should be comparable in value with the characteristic impedance and the optimum value is influenced by energy loss through radiation as the RF wave travels outwards. An average termination will have a value of approximately 800Ω. It is essential that the terminating resistor be as near a pure resistance as possible, without inductance or capacitance components ruling out the use of wire-wound resistors. The power rating of the terminating resistor should not be less than one-third of the mean power input to the antenna. For medium powers, suitable loads can be assembled from series or parallel combinations of resistors (eg combinations of 5 watt carbon resistors).

The terminating resistor may be mounted at the extreme ends of the rhombic at the top of the supporting mast. Alternatively the resistor may be located near ground level and connected to the extreme ends of the Rhombic via twin-wire feeder. The impedance at the feed point of a terminated Rhombic is 700 to 800Ω and a suitable feeder to match this can be made up of 16SWG wire spaced 300mm apart. The design of Rhombic antennas for 160m, 80m and 60m can be based on Table 7.1, considering them to be two V-beams joined at the free ends. The design of V and Rhombic antennas is quite flexible and both types will work over a 2:1 frequency range or even more, provided the legs are at least two wavelengths long at the lowest frequency. For such wide-band use, the angle is chosen to suit the element length at the mid-range frequency.

Generally the beamwidth and wave angle increase at the lower frequency and decrease at the upper frequency, even though the apex angle is not quite optimum over the whole range. Advantages of the Rhombic over a V-beam are that it gives about 1-2dB increase in gain for the same total wire length and its directional pattern is less dependent on frequency. The Rhombic can be easier to terminate compared to the V-beam. The Rhombic antenna's main disadvantage is that it requires four masts to support it and a significant area of ground to install it within.

## 7.3 The Beverage Antenna

The Beverage antenna [25] provides a mechanism for a directional MF reception antenna, however it tends not to be usable as a transmit antenna. The antenna was invented by Harold H Beverage in 1921 and comprises a wire span that is stretched out in the direction of the stations to be received and is installed low to the ground at around 1.5m. The concept of the Beverage antenna is shown in Figure 7.7. The wire span can be supported by plastic pipes spaced around 20m apart with the wire span held in place using cable ties. The antenna tends to reject signals from stations that are situated 'broadside' to the wire span in favour of signals from stations situated off the wire span's end.

The Beverage is a long antenna and the wire span is from about half a wavelength to several wavelengths in length. It is not uncommon for MF versions to start from around 300m in length, however shorter wire spans can give surprising results. Raising the antenna above the ground gradually changes the mode of operation of the antenna, with it gradually taking on the characteristics of a long wire antenna.

The end of a Beverage antenna is terminated by a resistor of several hundred ohms in value, with the other side of the resistor connected to a good earth system (see Chapter 4, where earthing techniques are described). This forms a travelling wave unidirectional antenna that is directive from the receiver end towards the termination.

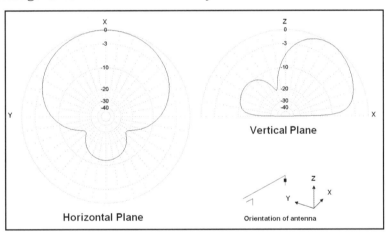

Figure 7.8: MMANA-GAL predicted radiation pattern for a Beverage antenna 630m long when operated at 472kHz.

### 7.3.1 Overview of Operation

The Beverage antenna relies on 'RF wave tilt' for its operation. At low and medium frequencies, a vertically polarised RF signal travelling close to the surface of the earth induces RF currents into the ground. The vector addition of the wave with the induced currents causes the RF signal's wavefront to 'tilt over' at an angle ahead of the oncoming wave. The effect of this is that the electric field is not perpendicular to the ground but at an angle, producing an electric field component parallel to the Earth's surface. If a horizontal wire is suspended close to the Earth and approximately parallel to the wave's direction of travel, the electric field induces an RF current wave that travels along the wire, moving in the same direction as the RF signal's wavefront. The RF currents travelling along the wire add in phase and amplitude throughout the length of the wire, producing maximum signal strength at the far end of the antenna where the receiver is connected.

RF signals arriving from the other direction, from the receiver end of the wire, induce RF currents propagating towards the terminated end, where they are absorbed by the terminating resistor.

The antenna wire, together with the ground below it, can be thought of as a transmission line that absorbs energy from the incident RF signal. The vector addition of the RF signal's wavefront and the RF currents induced along wire span creates a radiation pattern that has a main lobe off the end of the antenna. The result of this action is a unidirectional reception antenna. A MMANA-GAL [7] predicted radiation pattern for a Beverage antenna is shown in Figure 7.8 with the antenna modelled at 472kHz. The antenna modelled was 630m long, installed 1.5m agl and terminated in a 1000Ω resistor to earth. The horizontal and vertical radiation patterns show a large lobe directed forward off the end of the terminated end of the antenna.

# Matching and Antenna Tuning Techniques

The matching and antenna tuning techniques summarised in the following paragraphs cover operation on the bands from 160m to 60m. Matching techniques for operation on the 630m band tend to be more specialised and have been described within Chapter 3.

## 8.1 Balanced-to-Unbalanced (balun) Transitions

When an unbalanced feeder cable is connected to an antenna's balanced feed point, this can cause undesirable currents to flow along the feeder cable. These are referred to as common mode currents and they can affect the antenna's radiation performance, be a source of interference or a cause of problems from RF in the shack. An example of an unbalanced feeder is coaxial cable and if there is an imbalance between the cable and the antenna's feed point, then this allows common mode currents to flow along the outside of the cable's shield due to 'skin effect' [26] [27]. Therefore, if an unbalanced feeder cable is directly connected to an antenna's balanced feed point or to a balanced line, then a good practice is to use a balanced-to-unbalanced (balun) transition to avoid the undesirable effects that arise from common mode currents. For operation on the 160m, 80m and 60m bands there are two types of balun commonly encountered:

- transformer baluns
- choke baluns.

## 8.1.1 Transformer baluns

A balun transformer provides a technique to match an unbalanced coaxial cable to a balance load (eg twin-line cable or an antenna's feed point). Their use is often encountered with HF applications and many types of ATU use this technique to provide a balanced connection for a balanced twin-line cable.

Transformer-type (or voltage-type) baluns using iron powder toroid cores can be constructed to cover frequencies up to about 40MHz. These transformers have their origins in the work performed by C L Ruthroff [28] and function in the same manner as their lower-frequency counterparts. However, the low magnetic permeability of the toroid core allows these transformers to operate at much higher frequencies. To enable these transformers to work efficiently, it is important to maintain a high coefficient of coupling between the windings. To achieve this, the wires forming the windings are laid side-by-side to allow the magnetic field surrounding one wire to encompass the second wire so maximising the coupling. For efficient transformer action, the inductance presented must be large enough to ensure that connecting the transformer has no effect on the input other than that due to the load when connected to the secondary winding. However, there will always be some leakage inductance and this is usually considered as in series with the load. The leakage inductance increases in proportion to the transformer's self-inductance and these are functions of the coupling coefficient between the windings. Essentially, a transformer that works well at 1.81MHz may not work as well at frequencies above 20MHz and this often shows up as a worsening SWR as the frequency is increased.

To achieve a high coupling between the windings, bifilar or trifilar winding techniques are used where the turns of the windings are effectively wound tightly together with the wires usually in parallel. The concept of two transformer baluns for impedance ratios of 1:1 and 4:1 are shown as Figure 8.1(a) and Figure 8.1(b). The trifilar (1:1 impedance ratio) arrangement tends to increase the leakage inductance and this can limit the upper frequency range limit when compared to the bifilar arrangement (4:1 impedance ratio).

Peter Miles, VK6YSF has published several toroid iron powder core transformer designs based on the concept shown in Figure 8.1. These have included 1:1 and 4:1 impedance transformers with their details made available online [29]. Figure 8.2 illustrates one of these designs for a 1:1 impedance ratio transformer balun using a Micrometals Iron Powder Toroid T200-2 core suitable for use on the 160m, 80m and 60m bands. The 1:1 balun comprised 17 trifilar wound 3-wire turns with a small gap left between each turn as shown. A 4:1 impedance ratio transformer balun can also be made up in a similar way using a Micrometals Iron Powder Toroid T200-2, where 17 bifilar wound 2-wire turns are wound on the core with a small gap left between each turn. The wire used for the windings is not critical, however plastic insulated single core copper wire of 0.7mm diameter works well.

The SWR for a 1:1 balun can be improved at lower HF frequencies by using a 200pF capacitor connected in parallel across the transformer's primary winding where the coaxial cable is terminated [30]. However, this was found not to be necessary for the 1:4 balun in this case.

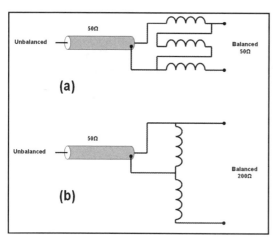

**Figure 8.1: Concept of transformer-type baluns. Windings (shown separately) are bifilar (2-wire) or trifilar (3-wire) wound on the core. (a) wire wound for 1:1 (trifilar); (b) 4:1 (bifilar).**

HF transformer baluns tend to be physically smaller than their corresponding HF choke type baluns. Therefore, their size and lighter weight makes their use at height feasible close to the antenna's feed point. However, a core should be chosen that is able to withstand the RF transmit power to be run and there are a range of toroid cores available from several suppliers or online sources. Most single T200-2 core baluns are capable of handling RF powers up to about 100W from 1.81MHz upwards.

To improve the power handling capabilities for a transformer balun, it is possible to stack two cores on top of each other forming a larger core. When using enamel insulated single core copper wire for the balun's windings, the toroid core should be wrapped with a layer of PTFE tape to insulate it. This is to provide electrical isolation if the enamel insulation breaks allowing the wire to make contact with the core. The windings can be held in place on the toroid core using cable ties.

When used outside, a transformer balun should be housed in a suitable weatherproofed box with the cables passed through sealed holes to the balun. The balun should be fixed inside the box using glue or cable ties to stop it moving around in turbulent weather conditions.

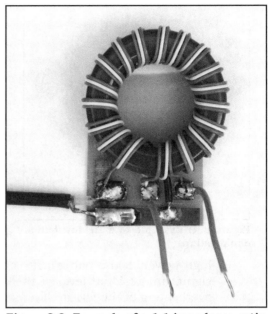

Figure 8.2: Example of a 1:1 impedance ratio transformer balun wound using 17 trifilar turns on a T200-2 core. This is a practical version of Figure 8.1(a).

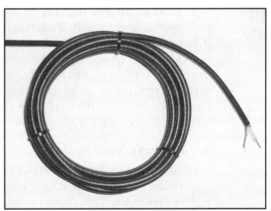

Figure 8.3: Example of a choke balun for the 160m to 60m HF bands made from coaxial cable.

### 8.1.2 Choke baluns

An HF choke balun for use on 160m, 80m and 60m can be made from several turns of the coaxial cable that are wound into loops to form an inductor. A typical choke balun is shown in Figure 8.3 and comprises around ten loops of the feeder cable between 300 and 600mm in diameter that are held together using cable ties. This form of choke is straightforward to construct, however it tends to be physically large.

It is possible to make a more compact choke balun using ferrite cores. This also tends to improve the frequency response for this type of balun [31]. Essentially, adding ferrite cores increases the balun's impedance in terms of both its resistive and reactive components (R ± jX). This in turn increases the impedance of the coaxial cable shield's outer surface, ena-

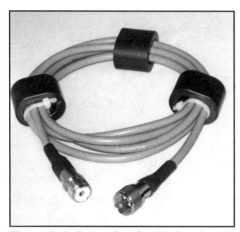

**Figure 8.4: Example of a HF low bands choke balun.**

bling common mode currents (Icm) to be suppressed to a low level. Ferrite cores also have the effect of increasing the balun impedance's resistive component, often exceeding 1000Ω. A high resistive component is desirable because this minimises the heat dissipated by the balun due to the common mode current flowing (ie $I_{cm}^2$ x R watts). An example of a balun covering the HF bands that used Fair-Rite 2643167851 or Farnell 1463420 ferrite cores is shown in Figure 8.4, while Table 8.1 summarises the construction details for this balun.

High common mode currents flowing along the coaxial cable's outer screen surface can be a problem when running high power. If the balun's resistive component is too low it can allow a significant residual level of the common mode current to flow, causing overheating of the ferrite. If a ferrite loaded choke begins to overheat, the ferrite may reach a critical temperature at which its magnetic permeability collapses, allowing an undesirable increase in current and causing even further overheating of the ferrite. When using high power, ferrite chokes with a resistive component of less than 1000Ω are at a greater risk of under performing and overheating. If the choke has successfully suppressed the common mode current, then the residual current value will be very low and it is unlikely that there will be significant heating of the ferrite. To make a good ferrite choke the right grade of ferrite must be used that is able to introduce sufficient loss at the operating frequency to minimise the common mode current and make its effects negligible. Additionally, for the choke to successfully work, it must have the right amount of coupling between the ferrite material and the magnetic field around the cable.

## 8.2 Antenna Tuning Units

An Antenna Tuning Unit (ATU) is a device used to provide an impedance transition between the transceiver and the transmission line, whose load is the antenna. The purpose of the ATU is to maximise the RF power transfer between the transceiver and the transmission line/antenna to ensure that:

- as much of the accessible RF power as possible that is supplied by transmitter is radiated by the antenna as an RF signal
- as much of the received RF signal as possible is made accessible as RF power for the receiver to function successfully.

Many of the antennas described will present an impedance that is not a good match to the transmission line. Similarly, the transmission line will present an impedance that is not a good match with the transceiver. The impedance presented by the transmission line will be influenced by the antenna's impedance and will often comprise a resistive and a reactive component (R ± jX). Therefore, the ATU is used:

- as a means to tune out and so neutralise the reactive component of the impedance connected at its input
- to transform the resistive component of the impedance presented at its input.

The effect of these actions is the ATU presents an acceptable output impedance to the transceiver that, in most cases, is ideally 50Ω resistive.

An ATU has to accommodate at least four antenna arrangements to interface the line/antenna with the transceiver:

- direct connection of a balanced or unbalanced antenna
- end-fed wire antenna worked against earth
- antenna fed with coaxial cable
- antenna fed with twin-line feeder or ladder-line.

A summary of ATU design and construction techniques for use on the 160m, 80m and 60m bands is summarised in the following paragraphs.

### 8.2.1 Pi-network Antenna Tuner Overview

The Pi-network ATU comprising an inductor connected between two capacitors was often used with older transceivers and has been included because many stations still use this form of ATU. The Pi-network has formed the basis of several commercially available ATUs, although the Transmatch technique has tended to become more widespread in recent years.

This circuit is theoretically capable of matching any transmitter to any antenna impedance (resistive or reactive). However, in practice the matching range is dependent on the component values used. For the widest step-up and step-down transformations, high-voltage variable capacitors are needed having low minimum and very large maximum capacitance values. Nowadays, obtaining such capacitors is not as straightforward as it used to be. The Pi-network possesses the advantage that it not only transforms impedance but also forms a low-pass filter, providing additional attenuation of undesirable harmonics and higher frequency spurii. The Pi-network was frequently encountered with valve radio transmitters and the concept of this circuit is shown in Figure 8.5 [32]. C1 and C2 are the tuning capacitors while L1 was often a 'roller-coaster' type variable inductor. Depending upon the load presented to the ATU, the tuning capacitors C1 and C2 are usually maximum value types of several hundred picofarads and rated at being able to withstand RF voltages of several kilovolts. This necessitates tuning capacitors whose plates are widely spaced to handle the voltages that can be involved (typically

| Band category | Frequency | Broadband choke details |
|---|---|---|
| 160m and 80m | 1.8 to 3.8MHz | 2 or 3 ferrite cores threaded onto a 5-turn coaxial cable coil of about 125mm diameter. |
| 60m band | 5.2585 to 5.4065MHz | 3 ferrite cores threaded onto a 5-turn coaxial cable coil of about 85mm diameter. |

Table 8.1: Summary of HF multi-band choke balun construction using ferrite cores.

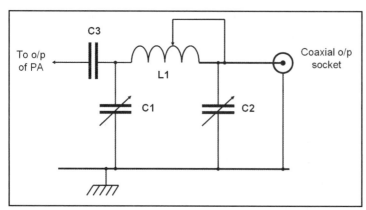

1.5mm or more). These requirements can now make obtaining such capacitors difficult. C3 is a blocking capacitor connecting the Pi-network to the output of the PA stage of the transmitter. Modern solid-state transceivers include integral low-pass filtering tailored to the individual bands, with the result that there is less of a need

**Figure 8.5: Concept of the Pi-network ATU used with older valve transceivers.**

for the ATU to attenuate undesirable harmonics as was previously required.

### 8.2.2 T-Network or Transmatch Antenna Tuner Overview

The T-network ATU can provide an acceptably wide range of impedance transformations without a requirement for large-value tuning capacitors. The T-network is a variety of the Transmatch, however it does not use the split-stator type of capacitor used by other Transmatch variants. The T-network's input and output ports are both unbalanced making its use suitable with coaxial feeder cables and unbalanced antennas. When the use of older valve transceivers was the norm, the T-network was regarded as a disadvantage because it forms a high-pass filter rather than a low-pass filter. However, now that low-pass filtering tends to be provided by the transceiver then this is less of a problem. While the T-network has become popular, it does suffer from losses at some transformation ratios on the higher frequencies. It is not uncommon for T-network to 'sink' around 20% of the RF power supplied to it depending upon the impedances it is expected to handle. This lost RF power is primarily 'sunk' by the inductor and care must be taken to ensure the T-network is not damaged when handling higher RF powers. These losses can be minimised by a simple modification of the T-network to an L-network using switches connected across the ends of the capacitors. The concept of a T-network that can be configured as an L-network is shown in Figure 8.6.

Referring to Figure 8.6, the value of the inductance L1 is selected to suit the band to be matched. This can be done by monitoring the noise level while in receive mode and varying L1 until the received noise level is a maximum, with C1 and C2 at their mid positions. Once the value of L1 has been selected, using a low transmit power, C2 is varied under load until a decrease is observed in the SWR reading. C1 is then varied to reduce the SWR still further. This is an iterative process, with C1 and C2 carefully adjusted until the lowest SWR is found. Usually a 1:1 match can be obtained. As a part of this process the value of L1 may need to be adjusted slightly up or down depending upon the values of C1 and C2. Once the combination of L1, C1 and C2 has been found for the band in use, the transmit power can be increased. However, good practice is to check that the SWR has not risen when higher transmit powers are used. Commercially available Transmatch T-network ATUs usually include a tuning chart to enable L1, C1 and C2 to be approximately set for the band in use, with their values adjusted to obtain the best match.

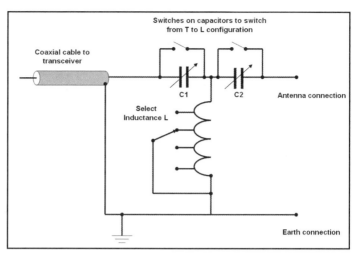

An example of a Transmatch ATU based on the T-network is the design by Mike Grierson, G3T-SOa [33]. Full construc-

**Figure 8.6: Concept of the series capacitor Unbalanced-to-Unbalanced T-network. This arrangement forms the basis of many modern ATUs. The shorting switches across the capacitors allow the unit to be switched to an L network to reduce losses.**

tional details of this ATU design are in the *Radio Communication Handbook* [34] and the following is an overview of this general purpose Transmatch ATU. The ATU's circuit details are illustrated as Figure 8.7 (overleaf) and the design includes:

- the capability to match lines/antennas in the HF bands from 1.8 to 28MHz
- the ability to match over a wide impedance range
- the selection of different antennas
- the facility to ground all inputs when the station is not in use
- the inclusion of an SWR meter
- a balun allowing the unit to be capable of handling balanced lines.

The values of capacitors required are not too critical and almost any high quality wide-spaced variable capacitor could be used. Ideally the variable capacitors used should:

- be between 200pF and 400pF
- be capable of working to 2,000V DC
- be of the type that uses ceramic end plates
- have a plate spacing of at least 1.5mm between the stator and rotor plates.

These requirements are necessary to cope with the high voltages that can be developed across the capacitors' plates when matching high-impedance long-wire antennas. Surplus variable capacitors that are in good working condition and meet the above criteria should be suitable for use.

The inductors can be either fixed, with a number of taps selected by a rotary switch, or variable such as the 'roller-coaster' type that allows the maximum flexibility in matching.

All switches used were of the 'Yaxley' type and use ceramic wafers. Paxolin wafers could be used, though they are not as good as the ceramic

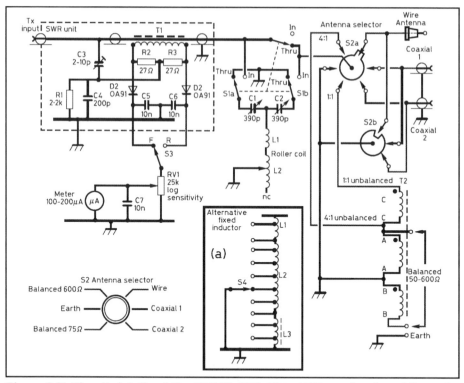

**Figure 8.7: Circuit details of the G3TSO ATU. This ATU was developed from the T-network variety of the Transmatch.**

type. The antenna selector switch used a double-spaced switch unit giving six stops per revolution rather than the usual twelve. The switch wafers were modified by removing alternate contacts. This modification reduced the likelihood of arcing between them.

Many of the components required for the ATU could be sourced from radio rallies, from online suppliers or from radio component surplus suppliers, although the latter are becoming fewer and fewer.

### 8.2.3 Balanced ATU Overview

Many of the antennas that have been described previously are balanced and so require a balanced feeder to avoid problems arising from common mode currents. Therefore, when an ATU is used to match a balanced feeder/antenna to the transceiver, the antenna connection terminal to the ATU also needs to be balanced. When the ATU does not have a balanced antenna connection, then a straightforward approach is to use a 4:1 or a 1:1 balun between the feeder/antenna and the ATU depending upon the impedance presented by the antenna/feeder cable [35].

Another approach is to link-couple or inductively couple the feeder/antenna to the ATU's main inductor. An example of ATU that was based on established balanced matching techniques was designed and built by Brian Horsfall, G3GKG [36]. The basis of the G3GKG design is essentially a link-coupled balanced Pi-coupler that did not require match selection through taps on the coils. This balanced input/output ATU design used one variable capacitor, C1, to 'tune' the network and a second one, C2, to 'tune out' any reactance at the feed point and match the overall impedance. The concept of the ATU circuitry is shown in Figure 8.8. Full constructional details of this ATU design are in the *Radio Communication Handbook* [34].

The two controls may interact, however it is possible to obtain a perfect match by rotating them alternately. Tune up was achieved by rotating each control until a decrease was observed in the SWR reading with the initial tune up using low power or with the aid of an antenna analyser. With practice it is possible to obtain zero reflected power, coincident with maximum forward power.

In general, the lower the impedance of the load the more capacitance will be required in C2 and, as the two capacitors are effectively in series as regards resonating the inductor, the lower will be the capacitance of C1. However, for either capacitor, the lower the capacitance when loaded, the higher will be the RF voltage across it at any given frequency and power. Furthermore, the lower the reactance in the load, the broader will be the tuning. It is only with very high impedances and highly reactive loads that the tuning becomes relatively sharp and critical.

There are three possible circuit arrangements of the two variable capacitors C1 and C2:

- C1 could be a twin-gang type with the frame earthed, to provide an 'electrical' centre about which the feeders are balanced.
- C2 could be a twin-gang type with the frame earthed, to provide an 'electrical' centre about which the feeders are balanced.
- C1 and C2 could be single-gang types that are completely isolated from earth with the whole of the secondary circuit, including the antenna system itself, 'electrically' floating. For this arrangement it is important that the control shafts are insulated.

In many amateur installations, the antenna will tend towards being unbalanced. Therefore, the latter floating method could be used where the whole feeder/antenna system finds its own 'balance'. For any of the cases above, high-value resistors should be connected to earth from each side of the feeder to prevent static voltage build-up. C2 will need to have fairly wide-spaced plates, although its capacitance does not have to be too high provided higher feed point impedances are avoided.

On the 160m, 80m and 60m

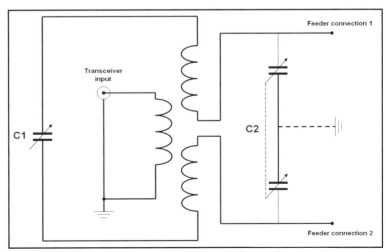

**Figure 8.8: Concept of G3GKG's balanced matching unit.**

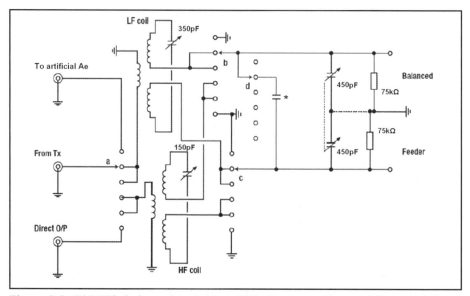

**Figure 8.9: G3GKG's balanced matching ATU. The two coil assemblies are: LF version (used for 80, 60 and 40m bands) – (9 + 9) turns of 16SWG tinned copper wire on 2.25inch diameter former, with 3 turn link of PTFE-coated wire. HF version (used for 20 to 10m bands) – (4 + 4) turns of B&W 1.75inch stock with 1 turn link between windings. A large, 4-gang, 6-way ceramic switch assembly a, b, c, d is used to select the bands). The capacitor marked * could be something like 330pF, but could be as much as 1500pF on 80m when Z = 75Ω (resistive).**

bands, the feed/antenna often presents a very low impedance to the ATU and the required value of C1 can be very high. This could necessitate either using a multi-gang variable capacitor for C1, with the sections in parallel, or additional fixed capacitors that could be switched in.

The full schematic diagram of the G3GKG balanced ATU is shown in Figure 8.9. Using this arrangement it was possible to make an ATU to cover 160m through to 60m (and the bands above), using two separate coils. This avoided switching the inductor 'hot' ends by having separate C1 tuning capacitors for each inductor (C1 as referred to Figure 8.8). The tuning capacitors used need to be able to handle high RF voltages up to several kilovolts and so their plate spacing should be at least 1.5mm. Similarly, the fixed capacitor should have a working voltage of several kilovolts.

The low frequency coil was wound on a ribbed ceramic former, with the turns closely spaced at about one turn's width. The coil's two main windings were spaced as far apart as the former allowed, giving a gap of about 25mm between the coils. Into this gap was wound the link-coil that was close-wound using thicker PTFE insulated wire and was kept fairly loose to minimise any capacitive coupling effect (that otherwise could produce an undesirable in-phase current in the feeder).

### 8.2.3 Other ATU Designs

The three designs summarised are representative of Antenna Tuning Units (ATU) in general. Several other designs are described in the *Radio Communication Handbook* to which reference should be made [34].

# An Overview of WSPR

## Background

Weak Signal Propagation Reporter (WSPR), or "whisper" as it is often called, is a digital communications mode that is used for weak-signal radio communication between amateur radio operators. WSPR was developed by Joe Taylor, K1JT, and is one of the digital modes available within the WSJT (Weak Signals by K1JT) suite of modes. Unlike other modes, WSPR has been designed primarily for beacon type operation. WSPR is designed for the transmission and reception of (very) low-power signals to enable propagation paths on the MF and HF bands to be assessed. But it is also very useful for experimenters because it can give objective comparisons between antennas.

## Operational Concept

Stations using WSPR transmit their callsign, Maidenhead locator and transmit power (in dBm) on a specific amateur band. Stations receiving WSPR signals on the same band can decode each station's information enabling the path details to be determined between them. The WSPR software enables the information below to be displayed for each station received:

| | |
|---|---|
| Date: | year (YY), month (MM) and day (DD) format |
| UTC: | hour (HH) and minute (MM) format |
| dB: | received S/N in the standard reference bandwidth of 2500 Hz |
| DT: | offset between computer clocks at Tx and Rx stations |
| Freq: | measured frequency of received signal (MHz) |
| Drift: | apparent drift of received signal (Hz/minute) |
| W: | spectral width of signal after removal of tone steps (Hz). |

The WSPR software allows successful decodes to be automatically uploaded to a central internet-based WSPR database [37] where every 'hit' is logged and a complete propagation map between all participating stations can be generated and viewed.

For the bands between 630m and 60m, stations using WSPR usually can be found within a 200Hz segment, as summarised in Table A1. Within Table A1, the USB frequency column indicates the frequency to be tuned to when using USB (assuming a 2500Hz bandwidth). WSPR is narrow band mode, therefore it is important that the transceiver's dial calibration is accurate to within at least a few Hertz (Hz) to ensure that the station is not off-frequency.

**Please be aware that the WSPR default frequencies for some bands, notably 60m, can cause transmissions outside the UK frequency allocations.** On some other (higher) bands the default frequencies conflict with the IARU Region 1 Band Plan.

### Transceiver Setup Guidance

The WSPR application is installed on a suitable computer and uses connections between the computer's sound card and the radio transceiver to enable them to communicate with each other. Once set up, WSPR decodes the received signals and displays the content. Similarly, on transmit, the software generates suitable audio signals that are passed to the transceiver for transmission.

For transmit, WSPR usually uses RS-232 request to send signal (RTS) to control the transceiver's PTT. Accordingly, the RTS function needs to be enabled within the transceiver's configuration menu, or it may be necessary to make a simple transistor switch to interface the PTT with the RS-232 RTS signal. If using the serial port to control the PTT is not a feasible option, then possibly the changeover to transmit could be achieved by using VOX (voice operated transmit) facility. If data modes are already in use at the station, such as PSK31, then the transceiver/computer probably have all the necessary connections already in place to support using WSPR.

### WSPR Technical Overview

The WSPR signal's 'payload' is a few tens of bits comprising the station callsign, 4 digit locator and the transmit power, which is specified to one of twenty levels (ranging from -30 to +30dBm). This is expanded to a one-of-four tone MFSK signal, with 162 symbols spread over a 110.6 second interval (110s). The effective total number of bits is therefore 324. WSPR uses a synchronisation code that is interleaved with the data stream in a pseudo random manner.

The 110s transmission fits into a two minute time slot (leaving just enough time for a CW identity at the end, where licence conditions require this). The WSPR software is designed for simultaneous transmission and reception of other sig-

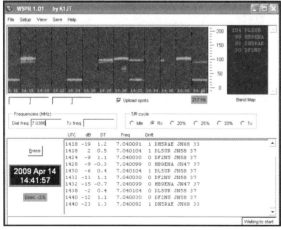

**Figure A1: Example of stations received using WSPR displayed on the computer.**

nals. To manage this, the transmit slots are allocated on a pseudo random basis as a fixed percentage of the total. This ratio can be selected by the user as 33%, 25%, 20% (etc) of the total. By randomising the transmit periods in this way, it minimises the likelihood of two stations clashing with each other every time and thus not hearing each other.

The tone spacing used is 1.46Hz. This is derived from the 12000Hz soundcard sampling rate divided by 8192 ($2^{13}$). The symbol duration is the reciprocal of this, or 682.7ms. This low tone spacing and with a bandwidth of 6Hz wide in total means WSPR is primarily used on the LF, MF and HF bands.

As WSPR was designed for signal reporting, some facilities were built into the software to give additional benefits. The WSPR software monitors a 200Hz wide segment of spectrum corresponding to tone frequencies from 1400 to 1600Hz and can decode every WSPR signal within this bandwidth. It searches over time as well to allow for errors in PC clock setting.

An example of the WSPR operating screen showing signals received is shown in Figure A1. The signal-to-noise (S/N) ratio is automatically measured in the decoding process and reported along with the message contents. As described previously, the WSPR software allows successful decodes to be automatically uploaded to a central internet-based WSPR database [37] where every 'hit' is logged and a complete propagation map between all participating stations can be generated.

## Antenna Experiments

Once you start using WSPR you will quickly be able to see how an antenna behaves, for example the location of 'spots' can give you some idea of the radiation pattern. If you make changes to the antenna you can directly compare the 'before' and 'after' results. Note that this is only really true over a very short timescale, for instance switching between antenna A and antenna B every few minutes. If you swap over a longer period then it's likely that changing propagation conditions will mask any change brought about by a different antenna configuration. However, if you run your experiment over a longer period – say a few days of antenna A then a few days of antenna B – you should also see some valid results. Although it should go without saying, to ensure you don't risk an electric shock or damage to your transceiver, make sure you don't swap antennas during a WSPR transmit period.

# References

[1] *RSGB Radio Communication Handbook*, 13th edition edited by Mike Browne, G3DIH: Section 10, Low Frequencies, Pages 10.20 to 10.40. Section 13, Antenna Basics and Construction, Pages 13.1 to 13.22.

[2] RSGB *LF Today*, 3rd edition, By Mike Dennison, G3XDV: Chapters 3 and 7.

[3] *RSGB Radio Communication Handbook*, 13th edition edited by Mike Browne, G3DIH: Section 13, Antenna Basics and Construction, Pages 13.3 to 13.4.

[4] IET (formerly the IEE) *Handbook of Antenna Design* Volume 2, A W Rudge, M Milne, A D Olver and P Knight. Published by Peter Perigrinus Ltd, 1983.

[5] RSGB *RadCom*, October 2012, LF column by Dave Pick, G3YXM.

[6] RSGB *RadCom,* January 2014, Operating on the 472kHz Band, technical feature by Mike Dennison, G3XDV.

[7] MMANA-GAL basic V3.0.0.31, freeware antenna analysing application. Original code by Makoto Mori JE3HHT. MMANA-GAL basic and MMANA-GAL Pro by Alex Schewelew, DL1PBD and Igor Gontcharenko, DL2KQ. 1999 onwards.

[8] *EMC 07 Protective Multiple Earthing*, RSGB. Available from the RSGB website (search for EMC 07).

[9] Spreadsheet for tapped loading coil design, weblink: www.wireless.org.uk/tap_coil.xls

[10] *RSGB Radio Communication Handbook*, 13th edition edited by Mike Browne, G3DIH: Appendix A, General Data, Coil Winding, Page A3.

[11] F6HCC's 472kHz project. http://f6hcc.free.fr/tx472khz.htm

[12] www.qsl.net/in3otd/variodes.html - on-line variometer design calculator

[13] 'Taming the End-Fed Antenna', Alan Chester, G3CCB, *RadCom* September 1994.

[14] VK6YSF Projects, Peter Miles, web link http://vk6ysf.com/unun_9-1.htm

[15] M0UKD Amateur Radio Projects, web link https://m0ukd.com/homebrew/baluns-and-ununs/91-magnetic-longwire-balun-unun/

[16] 'Eurotek', *RadCom,* September 1993.

[17] *RSGB Radio Communication Handbook*, 13th edition edited by Mike Browne, G3DIH: Section 13, Antenna Basics and Construction, Page 13.2.

[18] *RadCom* Centenary Issue. Published by RSGB July 2013. Pages 32 to 33.

[19] RSGB *Antennas Mastered*, by Peter Dodd, G3LDO. Pages 113 to 114, "A Simple but Effective Multiband Antenna".

[20] *RSGB Radio Communication Handbook*, 13th edition edited by Mike Browne, G3DIH: Section 15, Practical HF Antennas, Pages 15.9 to 15.11.

[21] RSGB *HF Antennas for Everyone*, edited by Giles Read, G1MFG, Chapter 1 Horizontal Antennas, Pages 77 to 80.

[22] RSGB *RadCom* Antennas June 2006.

[23] *The ARRL Antenna Handbook for Radio Communications*, 23rd edition edited by H. Ward Silver N0AX: Section 10, Multi-band HF Antennas, Pages 10.8 to 10.9.

[24] *RSGB Radio Communication Handbook*, 13th edition edited by Mike Browne, G3DIH: Section 15, Practical HF Antennas, Pages 15.41 to 15.42.

[25] *25 Simple Tropical Band and MW Band Aerials*, by E M Noll: Section 22 The Basic Beverage, Pages 49 to 50. Bernard Babani BP145. Reprinted 1994.

[26] *RSGB Radio Communication Handbook*, 13th edition edited by Mike Browne, G3DIH: Section 14, Transmission Lines, Pages 14.11 to 14.17.

[27] *RSGB Radio Communication Handbook*, 13th edition edited by Mike Browne, G3DIH: Section 1, Principles, Page 1.17.

[28] *Some Broadband Transformers*, C L Ruthroff MIRE, published by the Institute of Radio Engineers 1959.

[29] VK6YSF Projects, Peter Miles, web link http://vk6ysf.com/projects.htm, July 2012.

[30] Radio Communication Handbook 5th edition. Section 12 HF Aerials Page 12.42. Published by RSGB 1988.

[31] *RadCom* May 2010, 'In Practice' Pages 38 to 40, Ian White, GM3SEK.

[32] Radio Communication Handbook 5th edition. Published by RSGB 1988. Section 17 Interference, Page 17.8.

[33] *RadCom* January 1987, 'A General-Purpose Antenna Tuning Unit', M J Grierson, G3TSO.

[34] *RSGB Radio Communication Handbook*, 13th edition edited by Mike Browne, G3DIH: Section 15, Practical HF Antennas, Pages 15.13 to 15.24.

[35] 'Link Coupled Antenna Tuners: A Tutorial', L B Cebik, W4RNL, http://www.cebik.com/

[36] 'The doublet de-mystified', Brian Horsfall, G3GKG, *RadCom*, January 2004

[37] WSPR website and report database link: http://wsprnet.org/drupal/